Children of Courage

By

Charles W. Allen

Allyn House Publishing
P.O. Box 106
Nauvoo, IL 62354
Web site: www.allynhouseinnauvoo.com
Product and ordering information e-mail:
info@allynhouseinnauvoo.com

ISBN Number 0-9719132-0-X

Printing by Great River Printing, Hamilton, IL
Cover Art by Michael N. Rogers

To: Sue

Preface

I wrote the book, **CHILDREN OF COURAGE**, in order to share with the reader the experiences that I had, for nearly three decades, while my family and I nurtured and cared for my son and daughter who were born with Cystic Fibrosis. Being a husband and father in a medically challenged family, which included children born with terminal illnesses, produced difficult obstacles for me to conquer and unique opportunities to grow that were not possible to do under less intense circumstances. This is a narrative of trial and hope.

Cystic Fibrosis is a hereditary disease of the exocrine (mucus and sweat) glands of the body caused by a defective gene that was passed on to my son and daughter by their mother and I. The disease is characterized by the production of thickened mucus that chronically clogs the bronchi and pancreatic ducts, leading to breathing difficulties, infection and fibrosis. Many pancreatic enzymes involved in the breakdown and absorption of fats in the intestine are absent. This causes malabsorption, which is inadequate absorption of nutrients from the intestinal tract, leading to malnutrition. About one in 2,500 Caucasians is affected and one in 25 is a carrier of the Cystic Fibrosis (CF) gene. It is the most common cause of chronic lung disease in children and young adults, and the most common fatal hereditary birth defect affecting Caucasians.

Some of the common symptoms found in the afflicted child are: persistent respiratory infections (pneumonia), coughing and wheezing, weight loss, diarrhea, slow growth, easy fatigue, clubbing of the fingers and toes, and salty taste when licking the skin of an infant.

Early diagnosis of the disease and a disciplined treatment program can lengthen the survival rate and improve the quality of life for the child. Specialty clinics for CF are located in most larger populated areas and are associated with a hospital.

Current medications for treating CF include pancreatic enzyme supplements to digest food after it is eaten, and respiratory antibiotics for lung infections. Mucomyst can be used on occasion to thin the sticky mucus.

Additional important treatments include postural drainage exercises (PDE), which are performed by pounding on the child's back, sides, and chest to dislodge the thick mucus so it can be coughed up. Sometimes, percussion equipment is used, as well as other breathing treatments. Lung transplants have been successful in many cases.

Intense research continues to be conducted, which includes, locating genetic information to artificially insert a normal gene into the person. The ultimate success would be to eliminate the gene in carriers so that CF would never be passed on from parent to child.

The experiences that I have had with Cystic Fibrosis in my family validated the fact that it is a fatal disease.

Recently I was visiting with my cousin whose granddaughter was diagnosed as having CF. She was extremely worried and interested in visiting with me concerning my family's experiences and what she could expect. She wanted to know what her little granddaughter's future would hold. She told of the challenging times her daughter and son-in-law were having in adjusting to the diagnosis.

She showed me a book written many years ago by the parent of a child who had died at a young age from the disease. It was obvious that she had been studying it over and over as the book was worn with underlining and numerous notes written in the margins. I immediately recognized the book from the title as one I had read excerpts from years earlier. I mentioned to my cousin that I didn't share some of the personal conclusions that were expressed by the author, the most important being, that parents might want to medically terminate their ability to have children once they found that they were carriers of the CF gene. The author seemed to encourage this course of action. My personal experience has shown me that, if we had chosen to not continue expanding our family, we would have lost out on the opportunity of greater blessings and an improved quality of life.

I went on to explain to my cousin in detail of the many challenges that come to the parents of a chronically and terminally ill child, as well as to the extended family. One of the first challenges that can manifest itself is the parent's conclusion that their child is born this way because of something they (the parents) had done wrong. It is a natural tendency to look for something or someone to blame in this situation. Another difficulty to overcome is the temptation to view the child with the thinking that its death will happen at anytime. This is a very exhausting way to live, and most often produces over-indulgence of physical gifts and attention. It can wear the parents down so that it is impossible to earn a consistent income and create a wholesome family environment.

I told my cousin of the many opportunities her family could expect to have that would help them grow in understanding the suffering of others. This growth could develop into a strong and unrestricted desire to serve others who are experiencing critical situations.

Since I didn't agree with some of the conclusions

expressed by the author of the book she was reading, and was more than willing to share my family's experiences with her, my cousin asked if I would consider writing about them. For many years before she asked me to write about my experiences, I had seriously considered sharing what I knew in a public forum, such as a book, but the opportunity never presented itself. Now, however, I believe that the time has come for me to accept her challenge. I feel a need to share my experiences as a husband and father with the parents, families, and friends of those challenged by someone who is terminally ill or is faced with long term difficulties.

I begin my writing in the Introduction by explaining some differences in terminology and practices that are unique to the Church to which I belong. I have found that it is very important to have a healthy and meaningful spiritual relationship with Deity centered around, what I consider to be, sacred writings (scriptures). I also found that it was important to be involved with a Church or spiritual organization that provided comfort, knowledge, and understanding that was greater than the difficult experiences I was having. I needed a consistent source of strength. An understanding of the differences in Church terminology and practices is something I feel will help the reader to appreciate the experiences that our family had. This particular aspect of my story has been the main reason I have not written sooner about my experiences. So much of my life during my difficulties was centered around the spiritual beliefs that I came to understand and

I was hesitant to write about them as I felt it may cause disinterest with the reader. For this reason, I begin my writing by explaining these differences in church terminology with a hope that a basis of understanding can be gained that will make it possible for the remainder of the story to be understood and appreciated.

I next share with the reader the last few days of Camille's life. I quote from my daily personal journal which I have kept for many years. As imperfect as they may be, my journal quotes will be presented as they were written. I believe this to be a way to share a more personal view of events as they occurred. My intention is to quickly plant in the reader's mind the seriousness of Cystic Fibrosis and the agony that comes when I have to bid my daughter goodbye. I want the reader to appreciate the internal dynamics of a family in crisis and to understand that my writing is based upon my commitment as a husband to my sweetheart and a father to my family.

The next few chapters explain my background, my marriage, my first child's (Craig) birth and the emotional turmoil I experienced when he is diagnosed with CF. I feel that it is very important to share all aspects of my experiences so that the reader can gain trust in what counsel I might share.

I continue by writing of Camille's birth and near death experience as an infant and how my family rallies to her cause. I write of Craig's final days, including the monumental act of courage that he performed for his sister and family the day before he died. All through this, I share with the reader the struggles I have to provide a living for my family as well as the challenges my wife and I experience as we do all we can to maintain some semblance of normalcy in our home. You, the reader will find that my family and I have had special experiences that are of a sacred nature and we trust that they will be considered and appreciated with reverence and respect.

The final chapters include Camille's funeral when I take the difficult opportunity to speak to my family and offer my counsel.

My intention in writing this book is not to leave the understanding with the reader that a person has to be in a family unit in order to cope with and survive a terminally ill or long term experience. First and foremost, I want to convey the message that a person's success is directly dependent, to a large extent, upon how much and how often they will allow friends to become a critical part of their experience. It is a commonly understood fact of life, that when we are genuinely involved with each other in acts of kindness, our own burdens become lighter.

Charles W. Allen

No man is an island,
No man stands alone.
Each man's joy is joy to me;
Each man's grief is my own.

We need one another,
So I will defend
Each man as my brother,
Each man as my friend.

(Meditation by John Donne;
adapted by Bryan B. Gardner and Calvin T. Broadhead)

Introduction

In Webster's College Dictionary we find these descriptions for the following words:

Conscience: ...the inner sense of what is right or wrong in one's conduct or motives, impelling one toward right action.

Virtue: ...conformity of one's life and conduct to moral and ethical principles.

Agency: ...a means of exerting power or influence.

We can assume then, that *free-agency* would mean the unrestricted "means of exerting power or influence." When considering the above words and their descriptions, we can postulate the following example: *conscience* is the ability we all have to recognize right from wrong and to make the personal choices that will produce a *virtuous* lifestyle. *Free-agency* is the unrestrained ability to make those choices. Morally speaking, it is the second greatest gift we have been given to direct the greatest gift which is life itself. *Free-agency* must be used wisely. We are free to think, decide, and act but we must be prepared to accept the consequences of our actions, whether good or bad.

The world's historic landscape is littered with gross examples of the misuse of free-agency. It will always result in the unnecessary suffering of the innocent and unprotected. One example, of all too many, is Hitler and the Nazi regime who caused unthinkable suffering, to include, the Holocaust and loss of life on the battle front. Conversely, there have been efforts made by humble men and women who intentionally placed themselves in harm's way, with little or no regard for themselves, while leading an effort to alleviate suffering and to make their environment a better place to live. A positive example would be Mahatma Gandhi as he led the people of India in a peaceful effort to gain their independence and identity as a nation, and later died from an assassin's bullets. On a world scale, the misuse of free-agency is associated with dictatorship and tyranny, while the proper use of free-agency is identified with democracy. On an individual basis, the improper use of free-agency produces a life of selfishness and self-centered interests - - a "me first" mentality. The proper use of free-agency will always be centered in unrestricted and selfless acts of service to others. These examples can also apply to a family unit.

The principles we use as guide posts of information

for correct conduct have been generally established by religious leaders and spiritual movements over long periods of time, and adopted by faithful followers. This information is referred to as sacred writings or scripture (the revealed word from Deity to man), such as those found in the Koran, the Torah, and the Bible.

In times of great challenges in our lives, whether personal or societal, we tend to look beyond our mortal existence for comfort and understanding through an attitude of prayer. During these times we seem to be drawn to a need to pay closer attention to the moral use of our *free-agency*, and *conscience* and *virtue* seems to become a more important desire and need in our lives. This has been the case in our family that I have written about in **CHILDREN OF COURAGE**. Our decision making processes were based upon principles promoted in the sacred Christian scriptures centered in the Bible, and are practiced by the Church to which we have belonged as a family for seven generations.

In my writing, there will be references to practices familiar to those of the Christian faith, but there will also be some that will be unfamiliar, as they are based upon terminology and lifestyle indicative of members of The Church of Jesus Christ of Latter-day Saints. I will define some of those that will be unfamiliar in order to help the reader better understand some of the poignant experiences that I have had with my family. When I read that "last rites" were given to an individual, I can assume that the person was near death, a member of the Catholic faith, and had requested special prayers by the priest. I welcome the information as it helps me to understand and appreciate a greater depth of the experience. I feel no temptation nor need to ridicule a person for practicing beliefs that are typical to their particular religion. It is my hope, that by explaining some differences practiced by the Church that my family and I belong to, a deeper understanding can be gained by the reader of the experiences we have had. Where there are crises and trials, there will be a tendency to live our lives as they relate to our faith in the spiritual writings, practices, and information that we are familiar with.

Some practices used in The Church of Jesus Christ of Latter-day Saints that may be unfamiliar to the reader, are:

Paid clergy:

Somewhat different from many Christian faiths who have a paid clergy, the local leaders of The Church of Jesus Christ of Latter-day Saints are not paid for their religious service but conduct congregational affairs in addition to their normal employment. There is a local leader called a Bishop and he is supported or assisted by two counselors which make up a Bishopric. They preside over a ward (congregation). There are other local leaders who function under the Bishop's direction.

Priesthood:

All male members of the Church have the opportunity

to be ordained to the priesthood (the authority to act for God in Church procedures) which can happen as early as age twelve.

Young men are members of a preparatory priesthood and can be ordained to the greater priesthood after age eighteen. Those who are ordained to the priesthood have the opportunity to learn through their experiences while in the service of others. Husbands and fathers of the Church use their priesthood to preside in their homes and serve their spouses, families, and communities. The family is the greatest area of their priesthood responsibility. A worthy father can baptize his children into the Church and give blessings of comfort to his family and others when needed. Another area of priesthood service includes calling on several assigned families in the ward (congregation) each month to provide blessings and comfort. The women of the Church are not ordained to the priesthood, but they receive the same blessings as the men. They are not placed in a secondary position because they do not function in an ordained capacity. They do not need to be ordained to, nor hold, the priesthood in order to receive the greater blessings and rewards.

Eternal marriage and family:

As identified in Biblical scriptures, the family is the most important unit in society. The family is the basic unit in The Church of Jesus Christ of Latter-day Saints. In fact, the teachings of the Church are somewhat different than other faiths regarding the family. In our Church the family can become an eternal unit. It can be forever, literally. The Church builds sacred edifices throughout the world called temples. These buildings are different in their purposes than the typical meeting houses used for Sunday worship that are open to the public. The temples are open only for use by worthy members of the Church. In them the focal point of worship is centered in our Savior, Jesus Christ, and his gospel. In the temples, members enter into sacred agreements with Christ called covenants which obligate them to live exemplary lives patterned after his life. The focal point of the temple experience is for a couple to be sealed or married for time and all eternity. All activity in the temple is provided and presided over by those men who hold the priesthood with specific callings to provide these eternal blessings. All covenants entered into and blessings that can come from living them are predicated upon the faithfulness of the recipient. Members of the Church bind themselves in the temples to live Christlike lives within their marriages, families, and communities. The fact that a couple is married in the temple for eternity does not guarantee that eventual outcome. The worthy couple has to be married by one who holds that specific authority so that "what is bound on earth is bound in heaven" but the fulfillment of that possibility can only be realized by valiancy within their covenant to each other and the Lord over their lifetime.

Family Home Evening:

Throughout The Church of Jesus Christ of Latter-day Saints worldwide, each Monday evening is set aside for family home evening. There are no church meetings or activities scheduled on Monday nights. The fathers and mothers are encouraged to spend quality time in wholesome activities centered in an understanding of the teachings of Jesus Christ.

Through more than thirty years of experiences that my wife, Sue, and I have had in rearing our family of six children, it was vital that a proper understanding and use of *conscience*, *virtue*, and *free-agency* be adopted. **CHILDREN OF COURAGE** exposes our family's challenges that we are willing to share with the reader. These challenges, that are most agonizing at times, became rewarding over time in promoting and building character and commitment, both pillars of caring individuals, families, and society.

I, as Craig's and Camille's father, write from my perspective with numerous quotes and information from my daily personal journal. It must be remembered that each and every experience that I have had with my family was also witnessed and experienced by my wife. It was extremely difficult for her to give birth to Craig and Camille, nurture them for many years then hold them so lovingly while bidding them goodbye as they slipped from time into eternity. Also involved in the family were a brother, Marcus, and three sisters, Carrie, Christie, and Charlene.

It is our hope as a family, that by sharing these experiences with you, they will provide strength, courage, and hope to those who are faced with the similar challenges we have had. It is also our hope that you will find it is all right to go forward and experience difficult times, as these experiences can provide a pathway to true commitment and development of character. These experiences will present opportunities for pure service - - service well beyond restrictions of self-determined levels of convenience. It has been our experience that involvement in higher levels of service helps us to place the concerns and needs of others before our own. It causes us to feel that we are of real value to others. It helps us to feel genuinely good about ourselves with the unmistakable understanding that we can make a difference in someone's life - - their happiness becomes our happiness.

Jesus said of service: "Inasmuch as ye have done it unto the least one of these my brethren, ye have done it unto me." *Matthew 25:40 King James Version*

Chapter 1

Camille's health had declined noticeably since the end of summer and on November 16, 1994, her mother admitted her to the hospital in Peoria, Illinois, about 110 miles from our home. She had been treated at the Cystic Fibrosis clinic at St. Francis Hospital for the past several years. In September we had taken her to the lung transplant center in St. Louis. We were informed that she had a couple of months to decide before they would need to put her name on the waiting list as it would take 18-24 months for donor lungs to become available. Since September her condition had deteriorated faster then her doctor had anticipated.

Personal journal entry, Friday, November 18, 1994: "An emotional time as Camille struggles."

"I talked to Sue twice today. She said Camille is still very weak. I left for Peoria a little after 5 p. m. and arrived at her room at 7:15. She is so weak and frail. My heart aches for her. I am currently sitting in a chair by her bed writing in my journal. It is 10 p. m. Sue just left for the motel. About 8 p. m. I took her out to get some supper then I got her a motel room to stay the night. I will take my turn to be with Camille. It is difficult to sit here and see her struggle so. It brings back painful memories of the nights I would spend with Craig in the hospital in Kansas City at the end of his life. I wonder if he is near. He loved her so and was always looking out for her.

"It is now almost 4 a. m. (Saturday). I have been able to help Camille by getting her drinks of water and adjusting her bed. I just sit here and quietly watch her chest and abdomen heave about thirty times a minute trying to get air into her lungs. I do not feel I should sleep while she suffers so. I have never seen her in this condition. She has been in the hospital for three days and I don't see any improvement other than her fever is down and that is being controlled by antibiotics. I found myself asking Heavenly Father to please take her so she won't suffer anymore. Her attitude is one of sweetness. She has changed so much in the past three weeks. She has been so thankful and concerned for others."

Saturday, November 19:

"It is 9 a. m. and the sun is shining and the temperature is below freezing. When Camille's breakfast was brought to her, I coaxed her into sitting up to eat something. I cut up two pieces of french toast and she ate them.

She ate most of her cold cereal and drank much of the chocolate milk or hot chocolate I mixed for her. I rubbed her back while she ate and kept encouraging her to eat as much as she could. This is the most she has eaten at one meal in several days. She is so weak and fatigued. Her attitude is so sweet and her sense of humor is still there. I am so thankful for this.

"Sue arrived at the hospital about 10:30 a. m. after a much needed rest in the motel. Just prior to Sue's arrival, Christie called to check in. When she found out about Camille's present condition, she started crying and asked, 'Will she be okay?' She then asked me to give her a hug while she was still on the phone. I bent over Camille and gave her a hug then Christie asked if she could talk to Camille. I placed the phone on Camille's ear as she lay on the pillow. I heard her ask, 'Why are you crying?' It was an emotional and sweet experience. I couldn't hold the tears back. Christie talked to Camille for a short time then I took the phone back. Christie was very emotional. I told her I felt that Camille would be well enough to come home. I hope I am right. After Christie hung up, Camille asked me, 'Why is Christie crying?' I bent over and said softly in her ear, 'Because she loves you and is worried about you.' She said, 'I'm okay.' I told her that the only one not worrying about her condition was herself, then I gave her a kiss.

"Later this afternoon I called Christie to see how she was doing. She said she was doing better than this morning.

Sue left about 8 p. m. to go to the motel for the night. To me, Camille doesn't seem to be improving but perhaps the results from constant nurse checks will show differently. It just hurts me emotionally to see her struggle for breath this way."

Sunday, November 20: "Camille nears death."

"I did get some episodes of sleep during the night lasting about 10-15 minutes at a time totaling about two hours. I slept in a fold-out chair next to Camille's bed. She continues to fight for breath. She is so weak. When she sat up to eat, she said as she struggled for breath, 'I feel so funny.' It is a little after 8 a. m. and cloudy with light rain outside. Sue arrived about 10:30. Camille was sitting up in bed leaning forward on some pillows trying to sleep while her mother rubbed her back. I looked over at Sue and found tears gently flowing down her cheeks. There is a special and very strong bond between Sue and Camille as it is becoming apparent she is losing her battle for life. I can only feebly attempt to understand what it must be like for a mother to give birth to a child then watch while that very life she gave is weakening and preparing for departure.

"Sue stayed for about an hour then left for home. I was concerned for her safety given her present emotional condition but she said she would be all right. Soon after she left, Camille became nervous and worried. She said it wasn't directed at any one thing but she felt panicky. I felt so helpless as she started to cry. My heart went out to my Heavenly Father to help us through this crisis. The nurse was concerned and told me she put a call in for the doctor. It took him awhile to get here. Camille tried to further communicate her feelings to me. I got the feeling that she needed real rest, a good sleep. When the doctor arrived, he checked her and saw her weakened condition and felt what she needed was a proper rest to fight the battle. We discussed it and I told him I really feel she needs some form of sedation that will allow her to get several hours in a row of good sleep. He ordered appropriate medication. I rubbed her back while the medication was taking affect. After about twenty minutes, she wanted to lay back down and now is sound asleep. It is 1 p. m. I felt to thank my Heavenly Father for the understanding as to what my daughter needed.

"We have some problems! I am now sitting in the family area of the ICU (Intensive Care Unit) section of the hospital. After Camille was sedated her oxygen exchange rate went down. The physician felt that with her weakened condition and oxygen problems that she should be in the Intermediate Care section of the ICU. The staff told me I had to wait in the family area while they get her situated. That was an hour ago. I sit and I write. I was able to go see Camille about 4:15. She looked the same as when I last saw her. She is responding so much like Craig did in her weakness that it brought back very deep and difficult memories. I sat with her and let the tears flow.

"A little later Christie, Marcus, and Kathy arrived. We went to visit Camille. It was an emotional reunion. I knew what was going through Christie's and Marcus' minds and hearts. They have been here before. My heart aches for my family. They were able to tell her they loved her and she recognized them. We left the area hoping she would hold her condition. We returned to the waiting area to wait for the normal scheduled visiting time at 6:30 p. m.

"Marcus and Kathy returned from visiting Camille to say the physician wanted to see me. He said Camille's oxygen exchange is failing. They ran a test to confirm their suspicions. Before this sad news, I had called Sue and reported that all would be well through the night. Mike (son-in-law), Carrie, and Ashlie were at the house with Sue and Charlene. I talked to Mike and asked him to lead the family in prayer. Now that prayer is needed more than ever. The physician felt the only thing left to do for Camille was to ventilate her which means to induce a coma and put a tube in her lungs to supply her with oxygen. While they were doing that, I called Sue to report the sad news. It was so difficult for me. The physicians came out to report the tube went in well and during the procedure, large amounts of dark mucous were dislodged and they reported she looked better already. Oh how I hope and pray she will make it through the night and survive this crisis.

"Mike is driving Sue and Charlene to Peoria right now. Carrie is going to wait until Dave (son-in-law) gets home from work. I went to the restroom and knelt in prayer pleading for my daughter's life to be spared just one more time. I told the physicians I do not want them to prolong her life if it gets anymore serious or hopeless. They agreed to my request.

"It is 7:45 and I just went back to see Camille. They were working frantically on her as her blood pressure dropped. I pray the Lord will guide the physicians' thoughts and actions. It is now 8:15 and I received a call to the waiting room receptionist saying the physicians wanted me in the ICU. I felt this was the call I am not wanting to hear. As I walked back with Marcus following, I felt I would hear she was gone. When I got there, I was told she was now stable and things were under control. I was so relieved and was able to go to her bedside. I visited with Christie, Marcus, and Kathy about how I felt concerning what was happening and told them we must never be unworthy so as to be denied eternal blessings for our family. Christie asked me if I was afraid and I responded, 'No, I am not afraid.' Death does not frighten me but I do experience great sadness at the loss of the companionship of a close family member or friend. I can never come close to adequately express my feelings or even understand them when one of my children die. I made the comment to them that if Camille makes it through the night it will be because of Divine intervention.

"Sue, Charlene, and Mike arrived about 9 p. m. Charlene said she was afraid. I embraced her and said,

'I know.' They went back to be with Camille. It is now 10:30 and the waiting is emotionally numbing. This entire day has been one of emotional highs with a feeling of peace to a bottomless feeling of hurt and emptiness. It seems like there are only a few hours and sometimes just a few minutes between the peaks and depressions. It is now 11 p. m. and Carrie, Dave, Ashlie, and Maya (granddaughters) arrived. The Pierces loaned Carrie the use of their car. All my family is now here. It is midnight. This will conclude today's events. Camille made it to November 21."

Chapter 2

From midnight on, and throughout Monday, I was experiencing a roller coaster of emotions. Every three hours or so they would conduct a blood gas test on Camille. One time it would be a positive result and the next time she was headed in the wrong direction. Many of my extended family and friends called us during the day to express their concerns and love. Melva Hahl called from our home town to tell us the congregation at Church was conducting a special fast for Camille and the family. I greatly appreciated their desire to help in this way. The physicians continued to let us know throughout the day that Camille was in a very critical condition and that they were doing all they could for her. It continued to be an emotional waiting game.

During the day, Camille's regular physician met with us and discussed the possibility that he check out the transplant clinic in Chicago as he felt their waiting time would be less than the clinic in St. Louis. He made some calls and reported back that the waiting time was only a few months. He said he would like to continue fighting for Camille, and when she comes out of this crisis, he would like to see if she would agree to a lung transplant. He was very serious in what he wanted to do. I expressed my feelings that there would be little use in keeping her going if her lung capacity was insufficient, after the infection would be brought under control, to maintain her while she waited for a transplant. He agreed, then said we could evaluate our decisions as conditions changed daily, but that he "would like to give Camille a chance." I told him to go ahead. "... I am so weak and tired that I cry at the drop of a hat."

Mid-afternoon, Sue, Charlene, and I went to Camille's bedside and found out that she was not completely paralyzed. The physician informed us that he wanted to take her completely under so she would not fight the ventilator tube. This surprised me as I thought she had already been completely paralyzed since she had not been responsive.

Personal journal entry, Monday, November 21, 1994:

"I told him it would be fine (to take her completely under). A short time later Camille's regular physician met with us to report that she is affected by a resistant strain of a super bacteria and that has caused her present condition. They had been treating her for her typical infections and the tests they conducted last night showed what she has. He said there is no known antibiotic to treat her but he would try combinations of drugs to give it a try to find a solution. He then asked what to do if her heart fails, should they try shock treatment or another physically rough procedure to restart her heart. I said that I don't feel he should attempt it. He said he wouldn't do it. It was a difficult discussion for all of us. It appears her life is coming to an end. Only the Lord knows. We went back to see Camille after our meeting with her doctor and it was another emotional scene. We expressed our love to her, even though she is completely paralyzed, hoping she can hear us spiritually. As we walked away, we took the bags and sacks containing Camille's things and put them in the car. Sue was crying as she said, 'I feel I just said my goodbye.' Oh, how difficult it is! At 8:30 p. m. we went back to see Camille and had a meaningful visit with her doctor. I found out that even though she is completely paralyzed she can still hear and we were encouraged to talk to her. As Sue rubbed her cheek and talked so softly and loving to her she noticed a tear that formed in the corner of Camille's eye and ran gently down her cheek. Sue was very emotional and felt it was Camille trying to express to her mother how much she loved her. It was a tough moment. After our visit, I insisted that Sue and Charlene return to the motel to get some rest. I would wait in the family waiting area throughout the night and let her know if there is any changes in Camille's condition. The motel is just a few minutes from the hospital. A young couple, Donnie and Twyla Helvey, drove in from Davenport, Iowa, to spend the night with me. They are good friends of the family. The waiting room is a very emotional and difficult place at times. It was good to have the Helveys here with me."

Tuesday, November 22: "Our beloved daughter passes away."

"Sue called at midnight and was unable to get some sleep. I told her Camille was fine and that she needed to try and get some sleep. At 12:30 a. m. I went back to the ICU and checked on Camille. Things are still the same. She made it to November 22. It is 4:30 and I went back to see how she was doing. He temperature was going back up again and she has not produced urine. I retired to my usual place in the restroom and prayed that her body would function in this area. The nurse came back to let me know that I could spend more time with Camille. When I was first there the nurse started to swab out Camille's mouth and I left thinking she was going to do more things. I went back to her and stroked her forehead and face and told her I loved her. Because of all the electronic equipment and tubes around her, I wasn't able to do much but I did place my hand on her head and pleaded with the Lord to heal her. That is my heart's desire but I know the Lord is in control of the situation. It is now 5 a. m. Oh how a parent agonizes over a suffering child!

"It is now 5:30 and the nurse just notified me that certain things and tests indicate that Camille is failing fast. She thought I might want to notify family. I immediately called Sue at the motel and Marcus at home. My heart is very heavy. Sue and Charlene arrived a short time later and we went quickly to Camille's bedside. The Helveys were with us.

"We stayed with Camille to the end. She passed away at 7:03 a. m. My precious daughter has been gone fifteen minutes now. I explained to the ICU nurse of our religious beliefs and that fathers have the priesthood and I would like to give my daughter a father's blessing for parting and peace. The nurse stood quietly by with tears running down her face. Just before I gave Camille my final blessing, the x-ray technicians arrived with a portable x-ray machine to take pictures of Camille's lungs. I stopped them at the entrance to her room and said she has had enough and I wanted her to go in peace, that her fight is over. They left the area. Sue is talking to her mother while I sit here and write in my journal of things I really didn't want to ever have happen. Oh, my heart aches! I cannot describe the feelings I have at this moment but through it all, I am at peace - - the greatest blessing of all. The rest of the family is on their way. I will now go to make the calls I hoped I would never have to make.

"The rest of the family finished arriving by 8 a. m. and we went back to the ICU room where Camille's body lay. It was a tearful and emotional parting while saying our goodbye's. I bent over to give my sweetheart a final kiss on her forehead and lifted her head so Sue could pull her personal pillow out and take it with us. We left the ICU and returned to the private room the hospital staff had arranged for us. I spoke to my family and then we knelt around the table and I offered a family prayer. While we were meeting and praying, a Catholic priest was talking quietly on a phone nearby. He finished his conversation about the same time we finished our prayer. He asked to speak to me and said that he had been watching our family and was humbled by the way we reacted at our daughter's death. He said that we had a wonderful family with so much love for each other. I told him that we 'had been down this road before.' I hurt so much. I miss my daughter!

"It was a lonely, empty, and tearful drive for the 110 miles home. We didn't have that much to say other than how much we miss Camille and how Craig's passing thirteen years ago prepared us a little for Camille's death. No matter how many times I have this experience, it will always be a trying time to give up the companionship of a child. When we arrived home, there were many friends from the ward and neighborhood waiting for us. There was a meal prepared by the Relief Society. I mingled and made some calls to family and friends. I am so fatigued and emotional. Everywhere I look around the house I see evidences of the last days with Camille - - her carton of pop with two bottles yet to drink, etc. I am really saddened when I see her beautiful face on her graduation picture. Oh, what a beautiful young woman!

"Friends kept bringing food items for our family. Our refrigerator is full and other food is being taken elsewhere for storage. I worked on plans for Camille's funeral and burial. I made calls to Cameron, Missouri, where she will be buried beside her brother, Craig. As I look up at the clock from writing in my journal, I notice that my sweetheart has been in eternity for eleven hours. Time marches unmercifully forward. Carrie asked if she could fix Camille's hair and Charlene wants to do her make-up for her funeral. Carrie was really crying as she asked me and I told her, 'By all means.' Sue said she would like to dress her. It is now late in the evening and I cannot begin to tell of all the outpouring of feelings that we have received. Our phone was in constant use.

"I close this day, a most profound day in spiritual feelings and longings for my daughter. At the time Camille passed away, when her heart stopped beating at 7:03 a. m., I was standing on her right side with my hand holding her right hand and my other hand stroking her forehead. Sue and Charlene were on the other side holding her left hand. Donnie and Twyla were leaning against the window sill. The sweet ICU nurse was standing nearby quietly wiping her tears away. The last few days and especially this day are most difficult to record in my journal but it must be done. I just wish this had not happened, that her mother and I could have given her a better body that would have been free from Cystic Fibrosis. There seems to be a far deeper meaning to life and eventual accomplishments that could never be realized without this experience that will come to our family. Down deep I know that all is well but for the time being I have to adjust emotionally, mentally, and physically to understand and appreciate the better times that will surely come.

"As I sit here in my chair in my office, I glance over my stack of music tapes and I see the one titled 'Stand By Me' that Camille had given me for Fathers Day. It was the last present she gave me. Somehow that title has now taken on a new meaning. I need her to 'stand by me.' Go in peace my daughter. Your suffering is over."

* * *

When Camille died, it concluded a period of twenty-nine years and ten months that we cared for our two sweet children who were born with Cystic Fibrosis. This period began with Craig's birth in 1965 and ended with Camille's passing in 1994. Craig was a week shy of his sixteenth birthday when he died while Camille was nineteen years old. The emotional stretching and growth that took place during this time could never have been accomplished, at least for our family, in any other way. I have learned that adversity comes to everyone and it is through adversity that I could really learn and grow. In my life, uncomplicated times had never produced the growth that difficult times did, however, I found out early in my experiences that it is all dependent upon how I accepted my challenges. I found that I really could control my attitude during my trials and tribulations. Our attitude will determine how much, how quick, and how positive our growth will be. We not only have our free-agency, but we have the ability to make decisions of conscience and importance that will always produce mature growth and a genuine understanding of ourselves and others.

Chapter 3

I consider myself very fortunate to have been born into the circumstances that I was. To borrow an old phrase concerning parental worthiness, "I was born of goodly parents." In all the years I was in the presence of my parents I never heard them express harsh words or say anything disrespectful. Their relationship was not one of criticism or raised voices and they never argued. They loved each other deeply and demonstrated that love by their words and deeds during their entire lives. I remember perfectly a visit I had with Dad when I was eight years old. I asked him who the most famous woman in the world was. He smiled and softly replied, "Your mother is." He then went on to explain that some day I would find a sweetheart that would be that important to me. It was a special experience for me to hold my mother's hand as she was dying while listening to my father tell her goodbye and express to her how much he loved her during the nearly forty-five years they were married. She was sixty-one at the time of her passing.

Both of my parent's lives were centered in service. They were deeply interested in our family's welfare and made sure the children were reared in a wholesome environment. To me, it seemed that my needs and those of my brother and sisters were more important than their own. They displayed that same interest for others who weren't members of our family. To my parents, there were no qualifications or limitations that hindered them from doing something for someone else. My mother loved baking bread. She baked several loaves at a time. Later in the evening, Dad would ask Mom if he could have some of the bread she baked earlier that day. He found that there would be a loaf left for their use as Mom had delivered the rest of the freshly baked loaves to members of her family and friends in the neighborhood. I can still remember her coming to our house most always carrying a little paper bag that usually contained a box of Jell-O desert, pudding, or a can of vegetables that she got on special. During canning season, she was constantly preparing whatever was in season for others, keeping the smaller portions for herself.

On most nights, long after the rest of the family was in bed, a light could be seen in the eating area next to the kitchen. That was the time that Mom would do things for herself. While the clothes were washing and drying, she recorded her feelings in her journal and would write the longest and most interesting letters to family and friends. This was the time she could do a little reading. She would compile and revise large volumes of family history that she kept for each of her children.

During the night before Mom died, I was by her side visiting with the physician who was caring for her. She was unconscious, on a ventilator, and in very critical condition. The doctor said, "Charles, the problem is that we have a sixty-one year old woman in an eighty year old body." When he said that, a feeling of comfort came over me with the thought that my mother had literally worn herself out by serving others far beyond her level of convenience and endurance, and, it was all right. It was at that moment that I understood that it was acceptable to give our lives in the service of others, and that my parents had provided me with a worthy example to follow.

I was the oldest of seven children which included two sons and five daughters. I was born in Wyoming in 1942. When I was six weeks old, my father accepted a job offer near Spokane, Washington. Spokane was where I was raised, my brother and sisters were born, and where I consider still to be my home. My life during this time was typical. We had no major crises or tragedies.

I was ten years old when I saw my first television. That was when Dad brought home a new Dumont television set just in time for the Rose Bowl football game. Those were exciting times. I would run home after getting off the school bus and turn the television on and sit there with my eyes glued to the Indian head test pattern. The first program I remember seeing was a puppet show called Beanie. It was exciting for me to be entertained in my own living room. As exciting as television was, it still was no substitute for the Saturday afternoon double and triple features at the movie theater. The theater was always packed with noisy children as we anxiously waited for the drawing between features for a new Schwinn bicycle.

Prior to the coming of television, I spent some of my after-school time laying in front of the radio listening to my favorite programs, which included, the Lone Ranger, Straight Arrow, and Tom Mix. After the programs, I would hurry to my favorite place near our home that I called "down below the hill" where I would act out what I heard on the radio. "Down below the hill" was a short distance north of our home and was where I learned a lot about nature. I studied bird wildlife from books, then went to my favorite place to observe Chinese pheasants and meadow larks building nests, laying and hatching eggs, and raising their young. I built several birdhouses and mounted them in our back yard. The houses were generally occupied by tree swallows and bluebirds. I did all I could to keep the sparrows from living in them.

Late one spring, I noticed that a pair of bluebirds was not returning to their birdhouse after they had built a nest, laid, and hatched eggs. I took the house down and checked on the five hatchlings. They were still alive so I brought them, along with their house, into our house. We kept it in a warm place in the corner of the kitchen. Mom called the newspaper office in Spokane and found out what to feed them. For the next several weeks, she scrambled an egg a couple times each each day while I mixed it with milk and fed the birds with an eye-dropper. The little bluebirds grew up all-the-while looking to me as their mother. It was a sad and, at the same time, happy day when I helped the birds learn to fly in the backyard and then was able to turn them loose and watch them fly off on their own.

On Saturday evenings my parents would get me to take my weekly bath by bribery. If I didn't take it, I wouldn't be able to listen to the Gene Autrey radio program. Over my lifetime, I have come to appreciate those radio days because I have never had television invite me to experience imagination the way those old radio programs did.

I attended the same gradeschool and highschool for twelve years. At the end of the sixth grade, we moved to a neighboring school district. I dreaded the starting of the seventh grade in a new school. I was so miserable the first week I attended the new school that I pleaded with my dad to find a way to get me back with my friends at my old school. He thought that the superintendent might let me return since we still owned property in the old school district and told me that I would have to call him myself. At that age I was terrified of adults, especially those I didn't know. I was more miserable than I was terrified, however, and I mustered up the courage and made the call. I explained to him that our family had to move because the new four-lane highway was built through our home. We still owned the home since Dad bought it back from the state and had set it on a new basement a couple of blocks from where we used to live. After some consideration and thought, the superintendent gave his permission and the next day mom took me back to the old school. When I entered the seventh grade class room, all the students clapped and cheered. I was back home! I wouldn't have made a very good Army brat. I am most comfortable in a stable and consistent environment.

My dad spent a lot of time with me as I grew up. He was a carpenter and had his own home-building business. I worked during every summer with him, starting out as a very small boy. While we worked together, he shared his experiences while growing up in Wyoming. I heard a lot of hunting, fishing, and trapping stories. He excited me about sports when he told me of his experiences playing for his high school. He taught me how to hunt, fish, play marbles, and make whistles out of a section of green willow branch. He played baseball with me. He taught me to be a carpenter and to enjoy working with wood. As a very small boy, he made sure I was dressed appropriately for Church with a clean suit, white dress shirt and tie complete with cuff links, and dress shoes. He even had me wear a dress hat.

One important lesson Dad taught me was to pay tithing to our Church. I loved getting paid for my work in silver dollars. Dad knew I wouldn't accept paper money unless it was a five dollar bill or more. My pay for one period was three dollars. He gave me two silver dollars and one in change. He then showed me how I needed to set aside three dimes for my tithing payment on the three dollars I had earned so I could give them to the Bishop on Sunday. He made sure that I knew that my payment in tithing was for 10 percent of my gross earnings. The consistent payment of tithing over my lifetime has brought an abundance of blessings.

In both elementary and highschool, I participated in sports and lettered in football, basketball, and track. My high school basketball coach was Judd Heathcote who went on to win the the NCAA basketball championship years later at Michigan State University. My parents greatly enjoyed coming to watch me play sports. They never did push or overly encourage me to be on any team. Dad would only say that if it was what I wanted to do, then I needed to give it my best effort.

In my senior year, I ran the final leg of the two mile relay at a multi-school track meet. I was fortunate enough to pass the field on my anchor leg of the 880 and finish first. As I was catching my breath on the infield, I felt this enormous bear hug from behind. Someone had literally picked me up off my feet. Stunned, but curious, I quickly turned and found my dad with tears of joy streaming down his face as he hugged me. It caught me off-guard and I started to get emotional too.

In my senior year at highschool I was elected student body president. I was able to experience most of the opportunities there were in secondary school. I was a little above an average student as far as grades go. I excelled in the things I enjoyed and tolerated those things I didn't. The classes I did enjoy were mathematics, the sciences, geography, drafting, and architecture. My parents were involved in a losing cause to get me to do my best in all of my classes.

After highschool, I attended an out-of-state college for one semester until I turned nineteen years old. At that age, the young men in our Church have the opportunity to serve a two-year mission at their own expense. I volunteered and was called to serve in a mission located in the midwest. It was a new experience for me as I had never traveled beyond the Rocky Mountains. For the two years, I served in four different areas. I first worked in Illinois, then Missouri, followed by Oklahoma, and finally Iowa. As missionaries, it was our responsibility to explain our particular Christian beliefs to those who were interested. If they accepted the teachings they were invited to join the Church. We served in pairs or as companions and our instructions were very explicit that we were never to force our beliefs on anyone. Since the two years were paid for by myself and family, the mission experience taught me the value of sacrifice and service. Serving on my mission was the single most important experience I had up to that time in my life and prepared me for the challenges that lay ahead.

While on a mission, dating and social interacting with young women was forbidden. I served in Des Moines,

Iowa, for the last three months and while there, became acquainted with a young woman who listened to our discussions and accepted membership in the Church. She asked me to perform her baptism. Shortly after, I was impressed with a deep feeling that I had taught and baptized my future wife. It was an overwhelming thought for me to consider. As I was closing out my two years of service, the furthest thing from my mind was who I would be married to. Fortunately, I only had a month to go on my mission when I had this experience.

The young woman was Susann Eau Claire. She was eighteen and had attended nursing school for a short time. She was doing office work in Des Moines when we became acquainted.

She was born in Des Moines and raised in Mason City, Iowa, and was the oldest of four children, which included two sons and two daughters. She was raised by goodly parents that taught her to be responsible and to be dependable, which was appealing to me. Over the years, I have come to love and appreciate her parents and family as they have always been firm and consistent in teaching family values.

To officially bring my mission to a close, I returned to Spokane to report in to the local Church authorities. While I had been on my mission, my parents accepted a construction assignment for our Church that took them out of the country. They were living in Montevideo, Uruguay,

South America at the conclusion of my two-year mission. Since they were not living in Spokane, I only spent one day (twenty-three hours actually) before boarding a bus for Des Moines and an opportunity to become socially acquainted with the young woman I felt would become my wife. We dated for a couple of days then became engaged to be married. While we dated, she was living with her grandmother and I stayed with her aunt and uncle. We were only able to spend six days courting, then I was on my way to South America where I stayed with my family for a couple of weeks. Part of that time I traveled with Dad in Argentina. After the two week visit, I flew back to Miami and boarded a bus for Iowa for another three days of courtship.

When I left Kansas City for Spokane at the conclusion of my mission, I rode a passenger train for thirty-six hours. It was a 105 hour bus ride from Spokane to Miami and another twenty-three hours by prop-driven plane to Uruguay. I had a lot of time to consider the decision I had made that Sue was to be my wife. I was convinced that she was the one I wanted to spend eternity with and to be the mother of our children. It was my decision to sacrifice all that would be required of me to bring about her happiness.

Sue stayed in Des Moines to work while I continued on by bus to Lyman, Wyoming, and found work with my uncle as a carpenter building a custom home. About a month later, Sue moved to Salt Lake City, Utah, and started working in the radiology department at the Primary Children's Hospital. Several different times while I worked in Wyoming, I hurriedly cleaned up at the end of the day and took a bus to Utah, arriving about 9 p. m. I got to know the bus driver on this route and talked him into letting me off near where Sue lived. We would visit until a little after midnight, when I would jog to the bus station downtown and ride back to Wyoming, arriving a couple of hours before I had to start to work the next morning. I could only do this once a week. I would go to Salt Lake City on weekends but had a hard time waiting for another seven days before I could see Sue again. My uncle said that I had to be in love to be that crazy.

I moved to Salt Lake City later in the summer and rented a little apartment that we planned to live in after our marriage. I was able to get work as a laborer on a large construction project. Sue lived three blocks away in a large house with seven other single working young women. We set the date for our marriage to be September 12 in the Salt Lake Temple where we would enter into an eternal commitment to each other. Shortly before our marriage, Sue's parents expressed a desire to come from Iowa and participate in the ceremony. Since only members of the Church can enter the temple, and as her parents were not members, we sought and received permission from the president of the Church to be married civilly on September 11. Our Church accepts civil marriages for as long as the contract is binding. At death, civil marriages are terminated. The Church expects civil commitments and covenants to be honored by its members but also teaches and encourages them to seek after the greater blessings and eternal opportunities available to families.

We were married civilly on September 11, 1963. Early in the morning of September 12 we took Sue's parents to the train depot then hurried back home to put on our Sunday best clothing and drove to the temple to have our marriage sealed (joined) for eternity by one who held that particular authority. It was an awesome experience for me to look into my sweetheart's eyes and see the purity, wholesomeness, and love as we expressed our desire and commitment to each other, and the Lord, to live as husband and wife for eternity. Oh my, what a beautiful woman! How fortunate I was. Marriage took on a deeper meaning for us as we understood we were agreeing to a commitment that would transcend this life. I have always believed that our meeting and marriage was a direct blessing provided by a loving Heavenly Father.

During the afternoon following our temple sealing, Sue and I borrowed a reliable car from friends, loaded it up with my parents' camping equipment, and drove to Mirror Lake in the Uinta Mountains. I set up camp and left my new bride to herself while I took off looking for good areas to hunt elk. It clouded over during the night and there was a light cold mist falling the next morning. Our air mattresses went flat and our sleeping bags were not that comfortable while sleeping on the hard ground. Sue was dressed in several layers of warm clothing and stayed in her sleeping bag just to keep warm. I was loving the outdoor experience but she was not. She had caught a bad cold during the night and was having a hard time breathing. She was very uncomfortable and I finally realized that I needed to get her to a warm and more comfortable surrounding.

I took down our camp and drove to a warm motel in Wyoming where she could recuperate.

We only had two days to spend together and our first night in the mountains was not what my wife considered to be a positive experience.

Chapter 4

As soon as we were married, Sue's motherhood instincts became apparent and she was insistent on having a child. I, too, had the desire to become a father. We both were raised in a wholesome family environment and wanted that experience to continue with us. We had been married almost a year when we found out that Sue was expecting our first child. I was attending the University of Utah and working parttime. Sue continued to work fulltime at the hospital until her delivery date. I didn't register for the spring semester at school as I felt uncomfortable relying on Sue to provide the income for us while being a new mother at the same time. I went to work fulltime managing a service station for friends of the family. Early in the morning on March 14, 1965, Sue informed me she was having delivery symptoms and I drove her to the hospital. A few hours later she gave birth to a beautiful son. At that time it was not possible to know in advance what sex our baby would be. Since experiencing the birth of several grand-children over the years where we knew in advance what to expect, I am of the opinion that much of the excitement of having children is in not finding out what their gender is until they are born. For me, much of the anticipation is gone. Of course, the most important concern is the health of the mother and child.

I will always remember the first time I saw and held my new infant son. It was what I had hoped for, a son, just like Dad and Mom. I am positive I would have been just as excited about a new daughter, but this was great! It couldn't have worked out any better. Sensations shot through my mind I will never be able to completely understand or explain. For the first time in my life, my sweetheart and I had produced new life, an infant human being that resembled us, while at the same time having his own characteristics. I could appreciate the experience that Dad always reminded me of when he first saw me a few hours after my birth. All kinds of future experiences I was going to have with my new son flowed through my mind. I would be able to teach him how to hunt, fish, and play other games since marbles were not played anymore. I would play football with him and attend his sports activities. I couldn't wait to start teaching him what Dad and Mom taught me. But, first things first, we had to get him home from the hospital.

Our little son's head was covered with dark brown hair. It also had spots of lighter color that resembled a synthetic frost job by a beautician. I checked his hands and feet and made sure there were ten fingers and ten toes.

Everything seemed to be normal and healthy, tailor-made to be a future athlete. The name we chose for him was Craig - - Craig William. He just looked like a "Craig." A couple of hours after his birth, I drove north about forty miles to let my aunt and uncle know the exciting news. My uncle asked what we named our son. I said, "Craig William." My uncle said, "Oh that's nice, he has your middle name and initials!" In all the excitement I hadn't realized that mine and Craig's initials were the same. I felt even more proud and closer to him and his mother. After a hurried lunch, I drove back to the hospital to visit my sweetheart and little Craig William.

We were able to bring Craig home a couple of days later. Our home and lives would be forever-changed. I played the 5-string banjo as a hobby and would prop Craig up in the corner of the couch to play and sing for him. I am positive the first music he heard was the theme song from Beverly Hillbillies. Sue took perfect care of our son. She kept him so clean. We doted over him constantly while all kinds of thoughts of our future with him and other children we wanted to have were the topic of our conversations. We greatly enjoyed being parents.

Over the next few months, it became apparent that Craig wasn't feeling well. He had chronic diarrhea and acted like he was in a lot of discomfort. Sue tried different things to help him but nothing she did seemed to bring him relief. Also during this time, Sue found out that she was expecting another child. Its scheduled birth was to be about the time Craig would be one year old. We weren't expecting to be parents again so soon.

My parents returned after living in South and Central America for four years and we decided to go into business together in Wyoming. The first of December 1965 we purchased an old mercantile store in Lyman (where I worked with my uncle more than two years before) and made the move. I was to manage the business as Dad was involved in designing and constructing a new building for us to relocate our store to. He went back into the home-building business after we made the move to the new store.

Sue continued with the same physician that had delivered Craig so she drove 120 miles to Salt Lake City each time she needed a check-up. When the last of February came, we made sure my parent's Buick was always full of fuel in case we had to make a quick trip to Salt Lake City for Sue to give birth because our transportation wasn't that reliable. We didn't have to wait long. After midnight of March 6, 1966, Sue informed me it was time to go. I drove well over the speed limit and got her to the hospital in time for her to give birth to a beautiful daughter. She was about two pounds heavier than Craig had been and looked to be extremely healthy. Like Craig, she had a mop of long dark hair. Unlike Craig's, whose hair was wavy, hers was a mass of curls. We named her Carolyn Sue. Sue wanted to call her Carrie.

When I was thirteen years old, Dad came home from the

hospital and announced the I had a new sister and that he and Mom had decided to let me name her. That night I wrote the name Carolyn Ann on a piece of paper and gave it to him. He looked at it, and after some careful consideration, said he felt it was a little too long and suggested that I drop the "yn" and just make it Carol. He took a pencil and erased the "yn" off and took the paper to Mom at the hospital. Ever since that experience, I decided that if I ever had a daughter, I would name her Carolyn. I also wanted to name our first daughter after Sue and she agreed with me as long as she could call her Carrie. In a matter of months, we would find out just how much of a blessing our little daughter would become to us.

As Carrie developed from infancy, it was apparent to us, more than ever, that Craig was not well. She was robust and very healthy. Though Craig gained weight and had excellent motor skills, he didn't gain as much weight as he should have and he cried a lot. He still had the chronic diarrhea problem. Early in the fall, we took Craig to the closest physician in a town forty miles away. He checked him over and said, "Feed him a little paregoric, it'll go away." That has been a sarcastic retort in our family ever since then. We still find ourselves saying, on occasion, when somebody isn't feeling well, "Take a little paregoric, it'll go away." We tried it out and was not successful. We took Craig to a pediatrician in Salt Lake City and he suggested that we take wheat out of his diet. He also told us that if that did not correct things, he would make arrangements for more tests at the hospital. Removing the wheat didn't work either, so the first Sunday in October 1966 I drove Sue and Craig to Salt Lake City where she could stay with friend's while Craig was at the University of Utah Hospital for tests. I left the car with her and rode back home on the bus.

Sue checked Craig into the hospital on Monday where he stayed for tests. On Tuesday evening, she called me to report that the tests were concluded and we were to meet with the physician at 10 a. m. the next morning. Sue was not told what the results were but she did know that Craig was tested, among other things, for Cystic Fibrosis. The next morning, I rode the bus to Salt Lake City. Sue picked me up at the depot and we drove immediately to the hospital. The little guy was jumping around the bed and having a good time. He was so happy to see us. He was so excited when a city bus would pull up to the hospital. He'd say, "Atoss geeuumm buss!" (there goes a Greyhound Bus) over and over.

We walked into the physician's office for our 10 a. m. meeting where he quickly gave us the results of the tests and informed us that Craig had Cystic Fibrosis. Sue started crying as I asked, "What's Cystic Fibrosis?" I had never heard of it before. I found out later that the reason Sue started crying when she heard the test results was because she was vaguely familiar with the disease from her work at the hospital and knew that it was serious. We were informed that the disease was hereditary and was terminal. I said that nobody in our families had it. He said that we didn't have to have the disease in order to be carriers.

I asked, "How long do we have to be with him?" I was not expecting to hear the answer that I got. I will never forget those words: **"Your little boy will not live much past four years of age."** Sue was crying heavily and I sat there in a stupor. The future I had all planned out for our son was ripped to shreds. All that mattered in life seemed to come to an abrupt end as I made a feeble attempt to digest what I had just heard. I thought to myself, "Those kinds of problems are for other people; we didn't need this." In a matter of seconds a panorama of anger and frustration exploded through the full range of my emotions. About the only thing I didn't do was cry. Perhaps I should have, but my main concern at that moment shifted to my wife who was weeping uncontrollably. We made quick arrangements with the physician to come back at 1 p. m. to meet with the CF therapist and get the details of what we were to do next.

We walked in a hurry out of the office and to the elevator. We just couldn't bear to see our little son at that moment. I had my arm around Sue in a protective gesture as we entered and went down in the elevator. There were several others in the elevator who knew when they saw Sue weeping with her head laying against me that we were greatly distressed and had received some bad news. No one said a word as we descended to the main lobby. All we could hear was Sue crying. I hurried her out into the beautiful autumn sunshine and quickly across the road to a grassy knoll on the lawn. We sat down on the grass and just let the emotions flow. We sat there for a long time without saying much to each other while we looked down on the buildings at the center of the city a couple of miles away. We were both sifting through our own individual emotions as though going through some kind of a check-list. For me, about all I could come up with was a dead-end in every avenue of thought I tried to follow. It was a very difficult time as we sat there. I kept asking myself, "What happened to our future; what use is it to have any plans? How could my wife and myself pass on a death sentence to our children when we were both wanting a large family? What were we to do now?"

I knew I had to gain control of my emotions so I could be a strength for my sweetheart. We visited, though not many words or long sentences were used. Everything we did say seemed to be in quick and very short statements. Sometimes, all I could do was to grunt a response. We knew that we would have to go to our son's bedside soon. I was hoping, though unrealistically, that we would find out it had all been a mistake when we returned to him.

I will never forget the sight, or feelings, I had as we walked into Craig's room. He was his usual happy self, jumping and glad to see us. It surprised me as I, somehow, thought he should be taking on the look of death, like he was not going to live much longer. That was the time I allowed the tears to start to flow. I was a long way from coming to the understanding that it is good to weep. I was still living under the notion that real men don't cry. Over time, I would learn what it meant to be a real man.

And yes, it is all right to cry.

The therapist we met with was an older lady who was very nice and understanding. She never talked of Craig's inevitable death. We were introduced to digestive medications, postural drainage exercises, and how to operate and clean a mist tent that Craig would have to sleep in. We scheduled future clinic visits. During the afternoon, I made calls to the family informing them of the sad news. That was another time I lost control of my emotions. Those were difficult calls to make. Dad had taken some town youth to Rawlins, Wyoming, for meetings and was calling Mom throughout the day to see what was happening. When he found out what Craig had, he drove up into the hills in back of the city to pray and vent his emotions. It was a sad time for all.

We packed everything in our old car and got Craig comfortable in the rear seat so he could play with toys during the ride home. It seemed like it was a longer drive than usual. It still took a little more than two hours but it seemed a lot longer. We didn't have much conversation as we drove. Both of us kept looking around at Craig and quietly weeping and wondering what we were supposed to do now with our lives and our plans for the future. Things would never be the same.

Hunting during deer season wasn't the same that fall. I loved to hunt and get out in the wild. I had planned to have those experiences with my son when he got old enough to go with me but I knew, as I sat on a sand stone outcropping under the cedars in the desert or in the timber up on the mountains stalking deer, that what I had planned to do with Craig would never come to pass. I knew my priorities had to change.

Chapter 5

Craig was a year and a half old at the time of his diagnosis and Carrie was six months old. For a long time the thought kept going through my mind over and over again that I had the ability to cause the suffering and death of my children. Yet, we had a beautiful and healthy daughter that tests later showed was free of Cystic Fibrosis. So, it was possible to have healthy children. We were told that the chances of our children being born with the disease were 25 percent, with 50 percent chance that the children would not have the disease but would be carriers, and 25 percent would neither be carriers or have the disease. So far, we were one for two. Before Carrie was born, we were one for one. Somehow, these statistics were not comforting. Right now I had a son that was going to die before he was old enough to go to school and I had to come to grips with that.

For Craig's first Christmas, I got him a little red and white football jersey with the number 7 on it. I also got him a full-size football. I was going to have a wonderful time showing him how to play catch and we were going to have the choice experiences that my dad and I had when I was growing up. After I found out what Craig had, I wondered what use there would be of getting excited about football, or any other activity, when he was going to die. I packed up the memorabilia from my school days, that included news clippings and awards, and packed them away for good. I was starting to learn that those things were not the things that life was really made of. I was starting to learn that relationships were what was important, not awards and publicity. I was getting an understanding but it would be sometime before I could live it.

This was a very difficult time for my sweetheart and me. I thought I needed to be very involved at work because I was still learning how to manage a retail business that included plans for expansion. I found myself retreating and spending more time at work and less time at home. I left the day-to-day care of the children to Sue. I couldn't bring myself to come home early in the evening and hear the sound of the compressor providing mist for the tent Craig had to sleep in. It just tore at my heart. When I heard the dreaded sound, it reminded me of his pending death. It was a very difficult experience for Sue as I was not supporting her in the responsibilities at home. There were times I would sleep at the mercantile and come home for breakfast, just to keep from hearing the compressor. I was not able to get much sleep though as I would bunk out on vacant shelving a few hours at a time while worrying about things at home. I didn't take the time to realize what Sue's feelings were in adjusting to our circumstances.

Looking back now, I consider myself, at that time, to be very inconsiderate and selfish. She was the one who had to keep the mist equipment cleaned and running right. I did make sure the tent supports were built strong enough but that was about all I wanted to do. It was Sue who changed and cleaned the dirty diapers every day and sprinkled the digestive medication on Craig's food. It was a disgusting sight to watch as the enzymes started digesting his food on his plate if he didn't eat it fast enough. It literally turned his food to vomit. After a while, she started to mix his medication in a fruit drink, which he drank at the beginning of his meals, to avoid having to watch food digest in the open. Not only did she keep a clean home and care for a terminally ill son, she also had to keep up with a very active and healthy daughter. Through it all, Sue kept the children and home clean and in order. She was a wonderful mother and companion.

Before we found out what Craig had, we would go out on family picnics in the desert and hunt for arrow heads at ancient Indian campsites. We tried to continue with this and other activities but it was not the same. It is amazing what adverse information can do to, otherwise, normal and happy activities. I worried what people in the community would think. Then I worried that they should be more expressive to us in our difficulties and show more interest in us. It was discouraging to me to see other people happy. I had a hard time not wishing others would hurt like I was hurting. What I didn't understand at the time was that others were hurting and I was just not paying attention. Over time, I came to realize that the more I got involved with others during their challenges, the lighter my burdens and problems became.

I continued to avoid my responsibilities in the home as a husband and father for about the next year and a half - - until the summer of 1968. By then, Sue was so overwhelmed with the responsibilities she had to bear alone that she felt she needed to get away for a rest. She had been in the same difficult environment for all that time with little help from me. When her parents came for their annual vacation, she made arrangements for her, Craig, and Carrie to ride back to Iowa for an extended visit. I was so detached from my responsibilities that I didn't really care that they would be gone for awhile. At least I wouldn't have to hear the compressor and see the mist tent during that time.

The next weekend after they left, I was involved with the mercantile annual inventory that we had contracted out to a company that was in that particular business. The inventory was scheduled to start at closing time on Saturday evening and continue all through the night. It was my responsibility to have information on prices ready when things weren't marked correctly, or marked at all. The crew completed the inventory late Sunday morning.

As they were finishing up, Dad came by on his way home from Church and said he would like to visit with me. We sat down on the floor next to the magazine rack and leaned against the front wall. The store was closed on Sundays. He mentioned how difficult it must be for me to be a father to a terminally ill son. He went on to reverently express his feelings that Sue, too, was having an equally hard time of it. He also mentioned in a loving way that he felt there was more that I could be doing to support her in the home. He reminded me that we had a very healthy daughter and needed to understand that the children we might have in the future wouldn't necessarily be born with Cystic Fibrosis. Dad got my attention and helped me to admit to things I already knew but needed to be drawn out of me and dealt with.

What a special blessing it was to have a father who knew how to give correct counsel and help. In all my experiences with married life, my parents never intruded or forced their ideas on us. They showed us by their example as to how to live together. But now, it was time for Dad to say something and he did it in a most pleasant manner. Our visit lasted for about an hour. Afterwards I ate dinner with my parents then called Sue to let her know of my visit with Dad and the change it made in me. He unlocked the door that allowed me to lay my resistance aside of helping with Craig's care. We visited about my driving back to Iowa to get them in the next few days.

After our return home, we discussed the possibility of

having more children. Since Craig's diagnosis, it was our thinking that we were not going to have more children when we could cause them suffering and early deaths. We already had a son and a daughter. Under the circumstances, we felt that was enough. We were encouraged by many in the medical profession to have surgical procedures done to eliminate our chances of having children. This never was an option we would consider.

I started to reflect upon the special marriage commitment we had entered into five years earlier in the temple and our belief that our marriage and family relationship had eternal possibilities. The authority by which we entered into our marriage covenant had the power to "bind in heaven." Should we not demonstrate our faith in that belief and go forward and have more family? The old saying, "... it is better to have loved and lost, then never love at all," kept surfacing in my mind. After giving this matter much thought and prayer, I concluded it was necessary for us to go on and have more children. I presented my feelings to my sweetheart and she readily agreed. We made the determination that we would place our faith and trust in our Heavenly Father and go forward knowing that he would give us the strength to bear any difficulties we would be called to go through. The decision was not frightening for us, it just felt like it was the right thing to do. We knew that all, some, or none of our future children could be afflicted. We knew we were opening ourselves to difficult and painful challenges without ever having experienced the death of a child. We also understood that the greatest personal growth comes from difficulties. We would soon find out that our decision to move forward with our family would be greatly tested.

Later in the fall, Craig contracted a lung infection. He had been treated for episodes of the illness from time to time since his diagnosis. This time was different. He got progressively worse and would not respond to antibiotics. During the first part of November 1968 his fever became alarmingly high. We were in constant phone contact with the hospital in Salt Lake City. On Saturday night, I came home after work to find Sue wiping Craig down with rubbing alcohol. His fever had elevated to 106 degrees and he was unconscious. I helped her. We worked with him for a couple of hours to try and get his fever down. It was a very serious time and we both felt that his death was imminent. The physicians said we shouldn't drive him to the hospital unless we could get his fever down to 103 degrees. We got his temperature to 104 degrees and made arrangements for my sisters to take care of Carrie. I placed Craig on the back seat of the car for a quick ride to Salt Lake City. He was unconscious or comatose when I bundled him and carried him out. I had the feeling that it was over as we started out of town. I didn't drive very fast as I was dealing with the thought that if he was not already dead, he soon would be. There was a ground fog in the valley we had to drive through. When we got up on the "bench" to the west of Fort Bridger, we drove out of the fog into a clear, moonlit night. I glanced at Craig in time to see him open his eyes and look around.

He wasn't dead! I told Sue, "Craig is alive!" I increased my speed for Utah.

We checked him into emergency care and they immediately went to work on him. They wouldn't let us be with him but kept giving us reports that he was rapidly improving. About 3 a. m. they suggested we get some rest and we checked into a motel. Only the emergency staff knew where we were staying. We didn't notify our family. About four hours later the phone rang and I instantly assumed there had been a turn for the worse in Craig's condition. I answered it with trembling hands only to find out it was someone calling the wrong number. We were very nervous and concerned, so we got dressed and returned to the hospital to find Craig sitting up in his mist tent looking at a book. He had a cool damp cloth on his thigh to take the swelling down from several injections of antibiotics he had received. He was in a good mood and happy. We were so relieved and thankful that he had made it through the crisis. His temperature had dropped to a manageable level.

Craig stayed in the hospital for a few days while Sue stayed with friends. During that time she started feeling weak, and seemed to be getting weaker, so she went to the physician but could find nothing wrong. Craig was brought home just before Thanksgiving as he was over his illness, but Sue was still feeling weaker. A few days later, she got up in the night and collapsed, laying on the floor for some time. She was finally able to regain consciousness and return to bed and woke me up to let me know what had happened.

As soon as I could the next morning, I called the physician in Salt Lake City and demanded, "If you can't find out what is wrong with her, I will take her some place else where they can!" I was extremely frustrated, angry, and firm. I left Craig and Carrie in my family's care and drove quickly to the clinic in Salt Lake City. I had never been there before so they didn't know me personally. When I went in and said that I had just brought my wife down from Wyoming, they immediately got a wheelchair and brought her in from the car. Nothing wrong could be found but her increasing weakness and pale complexion bothered the staff and they suggested that she be admitted to the hospital for tests, and perhaps, exploratory surgery. It was determined that she did need surgery and, after about three hours, the physician came to me with a very serious look on his face. He picked up a magazine and drew an example on it of the reproductive organs. He showed me where a tubal pregnancy had taken place some time ago and had ruptured. He said they had removed a large amount of blood from Sue's abdomen which had been the cause of her increased weakness. He was amazed that her tolerance for pain was so high because she did not exhibit the classic symptoms related to this condition and explained it was a very painful experience. What really concerned him was that gangrene had set in and he was most concerned that he was able to remove all the decayed tissue. He said it was then a wait and see situation. He went on to thank me for getting angry with him and his staff earlier that morning as he was confident that, had we waited another twenty-four hours, Sue would not have lived. After surviving the crisis with Craig and now nearly losing my wife, I had a lot of things going through my mind.

After I visited my sweetheart in recovery, I checked into a motel and spent the evening in thought. I was forced to take a deep look at the decisions we had made recently to continue having children. In times like this, I would retreat to the scriptures for comfort and guidance. As I was pondering, the experience from the New Testament came to my mind of when Jesus healed a young blind man:

> And as Jesus passed by, he saw a blind man which was blind from his birth. And his disciples asked him, saying, Master, who did sin, this man, or his parents, that he was born blind? Jesus answered, Neither hath this man sinned, nor his parents: but that the works of God should be made manifest in him.
>
> *John 9:1-3 King James Version*

I looked up the particular passage of scripture and read it several times. As I did, the word "blind" was replaced in my thoughts by "Cystic Fibrosis." I was not conscious that I was blaming anyone about my son's condition but perhaps there would come a time in the future when I could. I had felt since his diagnosis that this experience was part of life and no one was at fault. Over the years, I have come to understand another meaning concerning the particular passage, "....that the works of God should be manifest in him." Yes, it was a great miracle that the blind man was given sight for the first time in his life. But other great miracles can take place over time in a family as they adjust to a challenge like this. An opportunity is provided for an increase in closeness and love that the family members can develop for eachother and the blind child, while teaching him to appreciate nature without the ability to see. They could find ways to teach him to see without the blessing of sight. It has been my experience that great miracles can come from the opportunities for changes within an individual and within the family. These experiences give life and relationships an eternal perspective and will change, for the better, the way we interact with others. Being reintroduced to this passage of scripture had a profound effect on me. While considering the challenges we were experiencing in our family, as it related to this scripture, I was absolutely sure that we should go on with our plan to have more children. Perhaps, "...the works of God (could) be manifest (in us)."

After a couple of weeks of recovering at the home of friends in Salt Lake City, Sue was able to return home in time for Christmas. It felt good to have the four of us back together and healthy. I enjoyed this Christmas as I stayed up all night to watch the three astronauts on television orbit the moon and relay breath-taking pictures back to Earth. This relaxed time only lasted a little while as several days later, and in her weakened condition, Sue contracted the Hong Kong Flu, which attacked the lungs with a serious infection and was spreading through the world in epidemic proportions. She was very ill for sometime but was able to be treated at home and, after several weeks, regained her health.

Chapter 6

During the latter part of 1968 and early 1969 my mother and sisters provided constant help by taking care of Craig, Carrie, and Sue. Much of that time, Craig and Carrie stayed with my family so Sue could complete her recovery. During the new year, our challenges seemed to be minimal but we were still wary of what could descend upon us without a moment's notice. Craig could get infection with a high fever very easily. We were warned by his physician that the Wyoming winters seemed to have an adverse effect on him. Sue and I had discussed several times during the summer and fall that we might have to look for a new area to live so Craig could have a better chance. My parents, too, were considering a warmer climate so Dad could continue building homes the year around. He was very busy in Wyoming but had to shut down during the winter months.

At the time, there was a national promotion for settlement in Lake Havasu City, Arizona, with free air transportation and lodging so a presentation could be made advertising the merits of the new city. My parents and some friends accepted the offer to visit the area. Dad was excited about the possibilities of working all year but he had some concern about the summer heat. We talked about selling the mercantile and our two families moving to Arizona to go into the building business. I investigated and found that the closest Cystic Fibrosis clinic was nearly 150 miles away in Phoenix. One of the concerns we had while living in Wyoming was the distance we had to travel to get Craig to his clinic. We felt that we needed to move where the clinic would be closer.

While we mulled over our possibilities during the latter part of the summer and fall, we continued to do special things as a family that had a therapeutic affect. There was a noted painter visiting the area during the summer who offered classes on oil painting. Actually, he was a relative of my aunt and uncle. I bought Sue a set of paints, brushes, and easel and enrolled her in the classes. She had a good time learning to paint mountain scenes. She is a good artist and this was a way for her to unwind a little.

While Sue was on an outing with Craig and Carrie on a nearby creek, she saw a muskrat swimming in the water. She mentioned it to my father and his excitement was perked. He pulled his trap line in 1940 and had never trapped muskrats since then. That was the year my parents were married and Dad's trap line provided an important part of their livelihood. After our move to Washington, he did trap coyotes for a couple of years when I was a little boy, but it had been a long time since he had a trap line set for rats and mink. Sue showed him the area where she had seen the rodent and he set some traps. He took Craig with him the next morning and found a trapped rat. He brought it back to the store and skinned it in the back storage room. I was watching all this and getting excited to go trapping, too. He showed me the dark spots on the rat skin which meant it was not a prime pelt yet. We waited a couple more weeks and tried again. This time I went with Craig and Dad and he showed me what signs to look for when muskrats move around during the night. He showed me the entrances to their dens in the stream bank and where they were digging for tubers to eat. He showed me how to set the trap just under the water surface in their pathways and to put a cut piece of apple on a stick several inches over the trap pan. When the muskrat stood up to get the apple, it would trip the pan and set off the trap. The next morning we checked the traps and found a rat in one of the traps I had set. Dad showed me how to skin it and this one had a prime pelt as there were no dark spots. I was excited. Dad suggested that I take Craig on my own trap line.

We ran our trap lines at various locations in the area. I was so hooked on trapping that many times I would go out after nine o'clock at night to check the traps and would find rats in some of them. I would reset them and go back in the morning with Craig and find more rats in some of the same traps. One day Craig had hold of a dead muskrat by the tail and walked into our kitchen. Sue was at the sink as Craig threw it on the floor exclaiming to his mother, "Here Mom, peel it!"

I greatly enjoyed the experiences Craig and I had together. It showed to me that things could be normal. It was my attitude that had a lot to do about how I felt. Although I realized this, I still had the nagging worry that he was going to die soon. He passed his fourth birthday and lived longer than the CF physician first indicated he would. Advances were being made in CF research that improved the therapy and treatment and the average age for the affected children was on the increase. It was my hope that he would keep pace with the average age. We were adjusting to our circumstances as a family.

One of my responsibilities was to drive our small truck to Salt Lake City weekly to get supplies for the mercantile business. Sometimes I had to make the trip twice in a week. Most times during 1969 I took Craig with me. Early in the fall, I was alone on one of my trips to get supplies. As I was driving, I was thinking over the possible move to Arizona with the concern that it probably would not be a good thing for us when a thought flowed through my mind that was like an emergency warning that comes across the bottom of a television screen. I can't explain it any other way. The "message" said, "Investigate Missouri." I thought to myself, "Why Missouri?"

Several years before, I had lived in Missouri while

serving on my Church mission but I never had a thought to move there. All day long and on my return drive home, the thought I had early that morning kept going through my mind. After I unloaded the truck, I returned home and shared my experience with Sue. In our discussions that evening we made the decision to consider moving to Missouri. I had lived in the Kansas City area (Liberty) for a time, so determined that I would make some calls the next morning.

I found out from Craig's clinic in Salt Lake City that there was a CF clinic in Kansas City. I made the call and visited with Doctor Burry who was director of the CF clinic at Children's Mercy Hospital. I felt good about what I heard and made my report to Sue. We made up our minds to move to Missouri as we felt the more humid climate and shorter winters would be better for Craig. We shared our thoughts with my parents as we all had committed ourselves to a business in Wyoming. We decided to sell out. My parents had changed their idea about moving to Arizona and were now seriously considering San Diego as they had visited there several times and really liked the climate. As we were going to move in different directions, and I had no investment in the current business other than my labor, it was decided that my parents would take what was left after the sale of the mercantile and use the proceeds to start a building business in California. I would leave town with my last pay check. It was my suggestion to do it this way. Sue and I felt that we were doing the right thing and that a way would be opened up for us to make a living. After several weeks talking to prospective buyers, the business was sold to a relative of the family we had originally bought it from.

During Thanksgiving week, I flew to Missouri. While staying with friends, I checked into finding a place to live and the possibilities for work. I also met with Doctor Burry at the Cystic Fibrosis clinic at Children's Mercy Hospital. During my visit with him, I had the distinct feeling that we were doing the right thing. I committed to a small rental home in the suburb of Liberty and returned to Wyoming to get ready to move my family. We rented a truck and loaded up our things and left for Missouri early Friday morning, the first week of December 1969. To start a new life for me and my family, my "grub stake" was my last paycheck of $325.

There was a very light snow falling as we left town, but it was not causing a driving problem for us. I drove the truck and Sue followed in our car. Most of the time, Craig and Carrie rode with their mother while our pet dog, Perrita, rode in the truck with me. Once in a while, one of the children would take a turn riding with the dog and I.

During our fuel stop at Rawlins, Wyoming, Sue mentioned that she was getting worried about Craig as he was not feeling well and his temperature was elevating. After leaving Rawlins, she couldn't drive very long at a time before Craig would get quite sick and vomit up mucus. I would watch for her to stop by the roadside in my mirrors then I would pull off and wait for her to start driving again.

We continued driving like this until she flashed her lights at me and we pulled off the road and stopped in a large gas station parking lot in Medicine Bow. I got in the car and she told me that Craig was getting worse. He really looked rough and it tore at my heart. He had been vomiting and coughing up large amounts of thick mucus, and his fever was getting higher. She asked me what we should do. I considered our options, one of which, was to check him into the hospital in Laramie about sixty miles ahead of us. As I thought for a few minutes, I said that we would go on and not stop. Down deep I had a feeling of comfort and peace that it was the right thing to do. Sue agreed and we continued on. As we drove passed Laramie, Craig quit vomiting and started to feel better and his temperature went down. I considered this experience to be the combination of a test and a blessing. We were committed to make the move to Missouri and that commitment was being tested. We had the feeling to continue on, and as we did, Craig was blessed to make a marked improvement.

We drove on to Cheyenne then turned south to Denver. As we approached the Denver area, it started to get dark and began to snow. We turned east on I -70 at Denver and it really started snowing. We were in a very bad storm. Fortunately, there was a Volkswagen bus ahead of me and I could see his tail lights. Even though it was difficult to see them all the time, I stayed close enough to see where he was going, but back far enough so as to not run into him. I was praying that he could see where he was going as his tail lights were the only things I could see to follow. Sue was having the same experience while following me. We drove under these difficult conditions for more than fifty miles. When we got to Limon, Colorado, we were very nervous and fatigued from the day's experiences. We pulled into a gas station on the west side of town to get information on lodging and were directed to a motel on the east side of town. The streets and highways were not cleaned off yet and the blizzard was brutal. We had a difficult time driving through town. I have experienced a lot of winter storms in my lifetime but never have I driven in such bad conditions as this was.

We checked into the motel leaving Perrita in the truck for the night. When we took our luggage into the room, we discovered that our checkbook, that had my last paycheck in it, was missing. I took the car and back-tracked where we had been, including the gas station we had first stopped. I knew I was not going to find the checkbook if we had dropped it in the snow. Within a matter of minutes, the drifting snow was covering up my foot prints. I returned to the motel deeply discouraged. While Sue bathed the children, I went out and got some supper. On my return to the motel, I happened to pull down the arm rest and found the lost checkbook and paycheck. It had accidentally been folded up in it during the time we were traveling through the storm. I rushed into the room with supper and the good news. We were greatly relieved.

After we ate, we had our family prayer and thanked

our Heavenly Father for our safe trip that day and for Craig's improved health. We prayed for protection and safety in our travels. As we were praying, the wind suddenly died down and all seemed to be quiet outside. After our prayer, I opened the door and noticed a rapidly clearing night sky with stars shining brightly. Tears welled up in my eyes as I felt that our prayer had been answered. I realize that the storm could have been one of those quick and violent fronts that moves through an area, but, with the timing of things I will never be convinced that it was anything other than a special blessing for our little family.

The next day, we awoke to bright sunshine and good driving conditions. We drove to Topeka, Kansas, where we stayed the night. On Sunday morning, we drove on to Missouri where several friends helped us unload the truck and get settled in our new home. We felt that we had been greatly blessed in our travels and Craig's health seemed to be stable.

Not long after our move, we took Craig to the CF clinic at Children's Mercy Hospital for his first visit and to get acquainted with Doctor Burry and his staff. During the first visit, x-rays were taken of Craig's lungs to begin his personal records at the new clinic. Sue was with Craig while he was being checked and I was sitting out in the lobby visiting with a friend, who was a resident physician on the CF staff that I had become acquainted with at the new ward (congregation) we were attending on Sundays. The x-rays taken of Craig's lungs in the Salt Lake City clinic, after his serious illness a year earlier, showed a marked increase in scar tissue buildup. Scar tissue buildup is permanent and reduces the lungs' capacity to exchange oxygen. When I asked my friend just how extensive Craig's scar tissue buildup was, he said, "What scar tissue?" There was no discernible scarring of the lining of his lungs! It is putting it mildly to say that I was thankfully shocked and overwhelmed. I had this strong emotion swell up inside me of profound appreciation. Sue and I visited at great length concerning the blessing we had been given. It had become one of those benchmark experiences in our lives. During the trials we'd had since Craig's original diagnosis, I was slowly learning that the Lord doesn't always remove challenging experiences from our path. What I was beginning to learn was that he gives us the strength to overcome those experiences which is our opportunity to grow and develop in character, determination, and commitment. We were learning, firsthand, that there needs to be a Divine partner to show us the way as our chosen path in life is impossible for us to travel alone.

Chapter 7

After our move to Missouri, we seemed to settle into a consistent lifestyle that was centered around the care of a terminally ill child. We were very conscious of the fact that we had a daughter that also needed attention. We couldn't neglect Carrie as we cared for Craig. Sometimes that was not always possible because Craig would need our physical attention as he struggled with illnesses at home or in the hospital. We never intentionally neglected any of our children.

A few months after our move, Sue found out that she was pregnant. On August 31, 1970, she gave birth to a healthy son. We named him Charles Marcus but called him Marcus. This is when we got the idea to continue naming the remainder of our children with a first name that started with "C."

Several weeks after Marcus' birth, we drove to the CF clinic at the University of Minnesota in Minneapolis to have him tested. The test for Cystic Fibrosis is based on the salt content of the child's sweat and infants don't produce much sweat. The equipment at the clinic in Kansas City wasn't that sophisticated as the child needed to be at least six months old for testing. We were greatly relieved to find that Marcus didn't have the disease. We felt very blessed and thankful that we had made the decision to continue having more children.

After our move, I was able to find parttime employment at J.C. Penny's through the holidays. After that, I worked in sales for an office machine manufacturer. Next, I worked for a concrete basement contractor. I was working for the contractor when Marcus was born. A month after his birth, I started working for a county surveyor. My responsibility was to break down the field notes, plot them on sectional control sheets, and send the surveyors back into the field to make adjustments. I loved the work as it required a combination of mathematics and art, both fields I do well in, but the pay was insufficient to sustain our family.

I worked at different jobs attempting to find something I liked to do, that was long term, and had sufficient income. I was finding it difficult to concentrate on providing for my family. I had this nagging concern that Craig could get serious lung infection at anytime and die and that worry kept me from giving full and consistent effort to most things. When I would leave for work in the morning, I'd have the thought, "Will my son be alive when I return home tonight?" This challenge plagued me for many years.

A couple of months after Marcus' birth, my parents visited us to see their new grandson. Dad was in the home-building business in San Diego and was very busy. As we drove around northwest Missouri, my parents were impressed with all the greenery and the sight of homes being built everywhere. Being raised in the West, we saw building going on only where there was a source of water for irrigation. Out here, Dad felt he could build a house anywhere he wanted because of the availability of shallow individual water wells. Besides, land was considerably less expensive in Missouri than it was in California. During our travels throughout the area, we became impressed with the town of Cameron which was about fifty miles north of Kansas City on Interstate 35. Dad and I made preparations to move there and work together in the home-building business the following spring. My brother, who was working with Dad in California, moved to Cameron with Dad and Mom to be part of our business.

Craig was attending gradeschool when we made our move to Cameron. He seemed to be getting along well while having a cold and infection once in awhile. When Carrie and Marcus got a minor illness, it was not a major worry to me, but when Craig got the same type of illness, I couldn't keep myself from wondering if this was the beginning of the end. Craig was still keeping pace with the national average age for the life expectancy of CF children.

While building several homes in the Cameron area, we bought our cabinets from a wood shop located in a small town eight miles away. We ended up purchasing the shop in December 1972 and I went to work in it building cabinets by myself. Dad kept building houses until he sustained a serious accident the following year. After his recovery, he joined me in the shop. My brother came to work in the shop at the same time Dad did. We expanded our work to include building custom doors and trim and we hired other workers from time to time as needed. A couple of years later, my sister and her family moved to Cameron when her husband was discharged from the military and he started working with us in the shop.

Marcus was a healthy and happy boy who loved to work in the shop with me. From time to time, Sue would come to the shop and help me stain cabinets, and as Marcus was still quite young and required an afternoon nap, we made him a bed in the plywood storage bin to sleep on. Craig would work with me too. I enjoyed having my sons and Sue work with me when they could. Sue really enjoyed Carrie's companionship, because she was teaching her the things she needed to know in the home to be a wife and mother someday.

Early in 1973 Sue found out that she was expecting our fourth child. Even during her pregnancy she would help me in the shop. In fact, she was helping me stain cabinets the day before she gave birth in December to a healthy and wide-eyed daughter. We named her Christina

Bronwyn. We loved our little family and felt greatly blessed that we could have four beautiful children. There never was a time when I felt at ease with life as I was perfectly aware of our challenges and that, at anytime, one of Craig's episodes of lung infection could quickly turn into a fatal experience. I was constantly burdened with worrying about Craig's future and the future of my family. I had a difficult time not thinking about, and even preparing for his funeral in my mind. I knew there would come a time when the pleasant times would end. I would never discuss this depth of my worries with anyone. I knew that Sue had personal worries that she kept to herself so as to not overly burden me and I did the same thing for her. However, we were not afraid to get into a discussion about what was needed to get Craig though a crisis.

Years before when I was on my Church mission, I listened to one of the leaders give counsel that included the Savior's mention of "...give us this day our daily bread..." in the Lord's prayer. He explained it in present-day terminology so we could better apply the principle to our lives. He said, "Yesterday is a canceled check. Tomorrow is a promissory note. But today is cash, and my young missionaries, the Lord deals in cash!" (President Spencer W. Kimball). His counsel was for us not to daydream or fantasize but to remain firmly anchored in today's activities, that this was where we would receive our guidance and blessings. We could study and retrieve things from the past and make plans for the future but we were not going to be blessed if we projected ourselves out of today and worried about something that had already happened or was yet to happen.

The need to remain focused on today's activities has been the most challenging thing I have had to do as a father of suffering children. It is very difficult to not relive past crises, and to not worry about future events, to include, the death of my children. I have had a very hard time remaining focused on "the present." However, when I am able to do this, I find that I receive the spiritual strength and guidance I need and my difficulties are not insurmountable; I find they are manageable. It seems that when I project myself in either direction from today, I deny myself the inspiration I need. The Lord never mentioned anything about "yesterday's or tomorrow's bread" in his prayer. He prayed only for "the bread of today."

During the summer of 1974 Sue became pregnant with our fifth child. At this time she was serving as President of the Relief Society, which is our Church's local women's organization. This pregnancy was different for her than the previous ones had been as she had threatened to miscarry. She was able to get through the crisis with medical help but she still had a nervous and unsettled feeling throughout the entire time of her pregnancy. She felt that her season of giving birth to healthy children was coming to an end.

Early in the morning of February 19, 1975, Sue gave

birth to a beautiful daughter who had, like all our other children, a head of thick dark hair. We named her Camille Eau Claire. Everything seemed to go well with Camille's birth and we began to feel that our previous concerns were unfounded. We were to find out very soon that our concerns were legitimate. After we brought her home, she drank nourishment but did not gain weight. In fact, she lost weight. Sue worked with her constantly trying to find something that she would be able to digest. We were biding our time hoping we could get her old enough to be tested for Cystic Fibrosis. For the month following her birth, I was under great emotional stress - - we all were! I had a feeling that our little infant daughter could have CF but I didn't know for sure. What else could it be that was robbing her of her life? I was in turmoil as I watched her waste away.

We made arrangements through Dr. Burry to take Camille to the University of Minnesota for testing. At the same time, a large snow storm blew through northern Iowa and southern Minnesota, shutting down Interstate 35. I found out that the next closest clinic that had delicate testing equipment was in Houston, Texas. We asked Dr. Burry to make quick arrangements for us to drive there. In our conversation with him, he asked if we would consider testing Camille in Kansas City just to see if they could get enough sweat from her to get a reading. If it didn't work, we could continue on to Houston. We were getting frantic and were willing to try anything that seemed reasonable. We took her for testing and they were able to collect enough sweat on the first try. When the reading was registered, it indicated that Camille, did indeed, have Cystic Fibrosis. She was seven pounds at birth, and when she was diagnosed, she was down to four pounds, eleven ounces. She had lost 33 percent of her weight in one month. Dr. Burry informed us that our little daughter was literally starving and was near death.

They worked with Camille throughout the day and found that she responded to a special formula in combination with digestive enzymes. It was difficult for me to watch the nurse place our fragile daughter on her lap with her head directed downward so a blood vessel would protrude on Camille's neck, then use a syringe to draw blood. The syringe seemed to be as large as our little daughter. I wondered if Camille would have the strength left in her to survive the testing. While she was being tested and treated, I made calls to the family. I called Dad at the shop to let him know what was happening and I became emotional as I told him that Camille had CF.

As Craig was not feeling well at the time and Camille seemed to be resting comfortably at the hospital, Sue and I hurried home later that night. We needed to get things prepared so we could take turns staying with her at the hospital. Mom was staying at our house with the children, and upon our arrival home, we were met at the door by Marcus with a very concerned look on his face. His dark brown eyes were glued on me as he asked, "Is Camille still alive?" It caused tears to well up in my eyes as I knelt down beside him and said that she was and that it looked like she would be all right. He was satisfied and ran off to bed. The rest of the children were asleep.

Camille improved steadily, and after a while, we were able to bring her home. It was on a Monday that we came home, so that meant it was family home evening. We were all together as a family again. During our get-together, we had Camille laying in a dry sink I had made in the shop that was just the right height and size for a new-born infant to lie in during the day. As we were having our fun time, Camille started choking and stopped breathing. Sue ran to her and picked her up. I told her to turn her with her head down and pound on her back. She did and dislodged some mucous which allowed Camille to start breathing again. We found out quickly that infants do not have the capability of coughing up anything. This meant that, for the next several months, one of us was going to have to be awake to watch Camille through the night. We decided to take turns to make sure she didn't choke again.

During the first month that we struggled with Camille's declining health, I was trying to keep my cabinet business going. I had a contract to build a set of kitchen cabinets for a client in St. Joseph, Missouri. I had committed to have the cabinets ready to install about the time we placed our daughter in the hospital. Because I was doing all I could to keep my daughter alive, I got behind on the contract. I called the woman to inform her that I wouldn't be able to get the set done when I thought I could, that I would be a week or two late. I explained to her that my infant daughter was near death and I had been involved with her at the hospital and with my family. I will always remember her total insensitivity to our difficulties as she said, "Well, that is your problem, you can forget building my cabinets!" I had some of the work done at that time. I never for a moment thought that there could be people with a total lack of empathy. It was a discouraging experience for me to go through. I wondered, "What kind of people could be so calloused so as to not understand the suffering of others?"

Chapter 8

It was very challenging for us during the first year of Camille's life. Much of that time, one of us needed to be close by where we could hear if she was choking on her mucous. Most of the time, it was Sue who cared for our little daughter. I would take turns with her during the night to listen for danger signals. Although it was impossible for either one of us to stay fully awake during our watch, we prayed each night that we would be able to wake up the minute we heard Camille choking. We were blessed to be alert and aware when she did have problems and were able to help her get through them.

Sue had given Craig his postural drainage exercises since his diagnosis in 1966 that would include pounding daily on his back, sides, and chest with cupped hands to dislodge mucus so he could cough it up. It was a new experience for us to use two fingers to gently pound on Camille. But it still worked and it gave Camille the opportunity to make it through some tough times. After a few months, she learned how to cough things up on her own and we were able to sleep a little more at night. I need to mention that most of the physical and therapeutic care that Craig and Camille received daily was done by their mother. She was determined and committed to give our children what they needed which, in addition to this, included appropriate time spent nurturing Carrie, Marcus, and Christie.

Camille gained in strength and improved to the point that, by the time she passed her first birthday, was fairly normal health-wise. Although she was getting stronger, she was still quite small for her age, and over the next few years, caught up physically with those of her age group.

During this time in our lives, we were able to adjust to our circumstances which included a lot of emotional growing. We found that we could carry on a fairly normal lifestyle with our family, which included, attending school activities, parent teacher meetings, swim meets, family picnics, special times with our extended family and friends, etc. During the later 1970s our family was blessed with fairly stable health. Camille never had the need to go back to the hospital for CF until the last two or three years before her death. Craig was sick at times with lung congestion and fever that required an occasional trip to the hospital for a tune-up. He missed a lot of school but was still able to keep up with his classmates.

One afternoon after school, he and Carrie brought their

report cards home to show me what their grades were for the semester. I must admit that Carrie was proud to the point of gloating as she had all "A's" on her card. In fact, she was waiting for me to pounce on Craig because of the poor grades he had earned. As I reviewed her card, I praised her for her wonderful grades and handed the card back to her. I then looked at Craig's card that had "C's" and "D's" (mostly "D's") on it. I also noticed that he had missed forty class days during the semester. I handed the card back to him and told him how proud I was of his good grades as he was still able to pass while being sick for all those days. I also told him that I knew of many days that he went to school when he didn't feel very good. I was very proud of both of their report cards and had a wonderful time letting both of them know how I felt. It was apparent that Carrie was expecting me to get upset with Craig and that she was disappointed when I didn't, but, when I explained my reason for being happy with both of their cards, they went away feeling very good about their efforts. It was a wonderful way to teach both of them what is really important in life. Our efforts are far more important than our accomplishments. On the whole, society is interested in us if we finish first and it is rare to find consideration for those who don't; we either finish in first place or we are labeled as losers.

About this time I had an experience at work that I was able to share with my family in a family home evening. It was a continuation of what I had told Craig and Carrie concerning their report cards. I had been building and selling dulcimers (stringed instruments) as souvenirs of Missouri and was considered somewhat of an authority on them in our community. A friend in town had built a dulcimer and wanted me to critique his work. I looked his over, played it a little and handed it back to him, as I asked, "Is this the best you can do?" He looked at me in a surprised way and said, "Yes it is." I told him that his dulcimer is every bit as good as the ones I build as long as I am doing my best, too. He was somewhat puzzled at my comment and felt his instrument was no where equal to the ones that I built. I was able to teach him of the way I believe, that, it is our effort that determines if we are successful, not what society judges as the best because of perceived superior workmanship and beauty.

Understanding the value of effort is one of the many blessings I have received from the years of trials that I have experienced, as I have adjusted and changed towards becoming a better husband to my wife, father to my children, and a servant to friends and society.

At the end of summer 1977 Sue informed me that she was expecting our sixth child. She had a normal experience during her pregnancy with no apprehensions or problems, and on April 15, 1978, gave birth to a healthy baby girl that we named Charlene Ruth (Ruth being Sue's middle name as well as her mother's first name). Two and a half months after Charlene's birth, we moved eleven miles out in the country to live on a twenty-acre farm that we rented.

During the latter 1970s I started to build windows,

doors, and trim for historic restoration projects. Most of those projects were located in Nauvoo, Illinois. I was also interested in designing and building energy efficient homes centered in geodesic dome principles. I used the wood shop to build historic items and worked out of my home developing the dome business. Neither one of these pursuits provided a very positive income for my family. We were really financially challenged during this time as we were affected by the national recession that was impacting the economy of the entire country. Interest rates skyrocketed and made it nearly impossible for potential clients to get financing. Dad was pursuing other things in the wood shop and he, too, was experiencing difficult times because of the recession. Actually, we sold our home in town to use the profit to satisfy business debt. We were determined we were not going to take out bankruptcy. It was a very difficult time for all of us.

Our first winter living in the country taught us that we couldn't afford to heat our farm house with a propane furnace, so we bought an inexpensive sheet metal wood burning stove and searched the area for available wood to cut and burn. The farmers in the area were more than willing to let us cut dead timber on their lands. A sweet experience happened one cold November Saturday morning when Craig, Marcus, and I were gathering wood. As I cut the logs up with the chain saw, the boys would pack them in the back of the pick-up. Craig was not feeling well and had to sit in the warm truck. Marcus, who was nine years old at the time, came to me with a serious look on his face and said, "I know Craig won't be able to carry the wood anymore, so I want to do his work too." I embraced him and thanked him for his willingness to work for his brother. There are many opportunities to serve that can come to a family with special challenges. Over time, the children developed a deep love and respect for each other. I, too, was continuing to change. One thing that I had done all my life was to keep my emotions to myself. I would not allow myself to shed tears or weep in front of anybody - - even in front of a member of my family. Soon, I was to have a special experience that would change my attitude about expressing emotions publicly.

As a hobby, I enjoyed reading American history and visiting historic sites. The area of Missouri that we lived in contained early nineteenth century historic sites that were important to the Church that we belonged to. My interest in locating these sites began soon after our move from Wyoming. In 1975 I was invited by a professor of Church History at Brigham Young University to do local research and try to find sites identified in pioneer journal entries from that period of time. I spent as much time as I could locating these sites and it provided a pleasing diversion for me. Many times I would be able to take my sons with me to tramp over an area. We really enjoyed the time we had together.

At the end of summer 1978 I was invited to accompany the president of our Church, Spencer W. Kimball, and his wife, along with others, on their visit to the area to explain what our current research had uncovered. During the day, President Kimball expressed his love and showed a genuine interest in me as a person. At the conclusion of our time together, he took both of my hands in his and asked me, "Would it be all right if I could consider you as though you were one of my own sons?" I was overwhelmed by his request. During the next few years, and up until the two years he was medically incapacitated before his death in 1985 at the age of ninety, we had a special and unique relationship. He was an extremely humble and loving man and communicated those feelings to me. He truly did treat me as a son. The most important thing he taught me was to be able to openly express my emotions to others in appropriate ways and to not be embarrassed by doing it. All my life I had been identified as a loner as to my emotional expressions. I felt that to openly express feelings through tears, somehow made me vulnerable and I assumed that I would lose control of an emotional situation. I learned from the special experiences I had with President Kimball that I could express sensitive emotions and everything would be all right and that I had been losing out on a very important aspect of life. **It was necessary for me to learn to weep.** I needed to overcome this personality flaw so that I would be prepared, with all emotional channels open and in working order, to be able to take on the increasing challenges and trials that were ahead for me and my family. President Kimball presided over a worldwide Church with members that numbered in the millions, yet, he found the time to spend with me that brought about a very important change that I needed to make. President Kimball changed me.

During the years that we had our trials, I looked for

inspirational stories about people who overcame great obstacles that I could gain courage and strength from. No matter what problem we may have, if we look around, we will find there are others who are faced with more difficult challenges than we are having at the time. About the time Charlene was born, I found the story of a man who had tremendous courage to overcome great tragedies during the mid-nineteenth century. His name was Stillman Pond and he helped to settle the West.

He and his family originally came from Massachusetts where they were living when they joined a religious movement (The Church of Jesus Christ of Latter-day Saints) and relocated to the western border of Illinois to be with other convert members of their Church. In 1846 the non-member residents of the area attacked and drove the people, including the Pond family, from their settlement and out onto the plains of the southern Iowa Territory, and this began the greatest group migration in our nation's history. The Pond family, which included Stillman, his wife and seven children, left in September and traveled by walking alongside their horse-drawn wagon. The conditions were brutal as winter came early that year. Their destination was the west bank of the Missouri River near where Omaha, Nebraska, is today. It was the designated gathering site for those making the trek West to quarter or live temporarily through the winter. In fact, it was called Winter Quarters; in 1846 it was located in Indian territory.

As the Pond family traveled through southern Iowa,

the mother contracted consumption (tuberculosis) while all seven children were stricken with malaria. Stillman's wife was heavy with child and, in her weakened condition, gave birth to twin sons. Because of the difficult weather conditions, the twin babies died and were buried along the trail. While still traveling across Iowa, three more children died and were buried.

The Stillman Pond family finally arrived in Winter Quarters, and like the others who had been driven from their homes in Illinois, suffered during the winter while living in a make-shift shelter. The family lived through the winter and the following spring in a tent and suffered bitterly as the four remaining children died from malaria and were buried in shallow graves in the frozen ground. In May 1847 Stillman's wife died. In a period of eight months, he had buried all nine of his children ranging in ages from infancy to eighteen years old, and finally, he buried his sweetheart. In agony, but undeterred, he continued on to the West with other pioneers, who suffered like he had, and became a settler in the Rocky Mountains. He remarried and had another family which numbers many descendants today.

The story of the Stillman Pond family had given me a reason to keep on going, no matter what the conditions or circumstances might be. Yes, he suffered loss through brutal conditions that could have been averted had he and his family not been driven out of their homes and community by mob action. What provided me with an increased appreciation was the fact that Stillman Pond could have ended his suffering by denouncing his new-found religion and returned to Massachusetts. This he never did as his convictions were deeper than life itself. My wife and I had made the decision to continue having children, and learning of Stillman Pond's convictions and what he suffered because of them, and the blessings that ultimately came to him, validated our decision.

> Here then is a great truth. In the pain, the agony, and the heroic endeavors of life, we pass through a refiner's fire, and the insignificant and the unimportant in our lives can melt away like dross and make our faith bright, intact, and strong. In this way the divine image can be mirrored from the soul. It is part of the purging toll exacted of some to become acquainted with God. In the agonies of life, we seem to listen better to the faint, godly whisperings of the Divine Shepherd.
>
> *James E. Faust, 1978*

Chapter 9

Other challenges surfaced in our immediate family. At fifty-four years if age, my mother was diagnosed with a rare form of lymph cancer and was told she had about seven years to live. My younger sister, Judy, whose husband was working with us in the shop, was diagnosed at about the same time with cancer of the liver and pancreas, and her future was predicted by the physicians to be shorter than that of my mother's. Judy and her husband were the parents of five sweet children at the time of her diagnosis. As a family, we needed to rally our support for Mom and my sister.

At the end of the 1970s Craig's condition worsened requiring that he be hospitalized more frequently. During this same time, the economic down-turn in the country was really causing financial problems for our family. Fortunately, for most of the time, Craig's illness was paid for by the Missouri Crippled Children's Association. However, there would be an occasional funding lapse that would last for a long period of time and the hospital bills would mount up to a considerable sum and be turned over to a collection agency. I would be pressed for payment while the best I could do was to barely eek out an income to cover our basic necessities. I would explain my situation to the debt collection companies and try to keep them informed until additional funding would come to the association. I never had any extra money that I could send to them. It was a challenging experience to try and keep a positive attitude about our conditions. Many friends and extended family came to our aid with food, firewood, hand-me-down clothing, and money for utilities. The winters during this period of time were very harsh in our part of the country. I would watch the weather report and if the forecast was to be twenty degrees or colder, I would sleep on the living room floor on the couch cushions dressed only in underclothing with a thin sheet to cover me. It was not possible to bank the wood burning stove for the night so I slept on the floor to watch the fire. With thin covering and clothing, I would awaken twice during the night (first between 11:00 and midnight, and again between 4:00 and 5:00 in the morning) to put new pieces of wood on the fire. There was one stretch of time when I was on the floor for nearly three weeks. It seemed that most of my wintertime was spent gathering, splitting, and stacking wood and keeping the stove going through the cold nights. Sue and I also took turns staying with Craig at the hospital in Kansas City.

As Craig's condition worsened, our family's concern

and love for him deepened. Charlene was about two years old then and Craig really enjoyed calming her down when no one else could. When it was time for bed, and when he was not in the hospital, he would take her upstairs to his little bedroom and read to her until she would fall asleep. He was so tender and loving with a deep understanding for what people needed. He would make the quietest suggestions that would always be correct.

With each hospitalization, we knew that our son was getting closer to death. Admitting Craig to the hospital was a increasingly difficult thing for me to do as he would be on the same floor with terminally ill children and I could see for myself, by watching other children, what was in store for him and our family. It was very discouraging and heart-wrenching. Our conversations with Dr. Burry and his staff became more centered on how to give Craig a quality life with what time he had left. The physicians never really brought up the fact that Craig's life would end soon as that seemed to be left for us to consider. They understood that we had a greater understanding for what was going on emotionally in our family and with Craig. I did ask one of the resident physicians what I could expect as things got worse. I wanted to know for myself how Craig would be affected and how he would medically react to those phases near the end. I never shared this conversation nor my findings with Sue.

Also during this time, we became very close friends with a sweet family, the Tuckers, who lived in the

Kansas City area. They became intrigued with the geodesic dome homes I had designed. They were also interested in helping our family cope with our struggles. Whenever I would stop by their home, Agnes would fill up a large paper bag with meat from her freezer to take home to my family. Horace became a valued friend for me. The Tuckers were raised in difficult circumstances and really had an understanding of the challenges that life has to offer. They seemed to be the family that the Lord sent to us at that time in our lives to give us the comfort and courage that we needed.

For Christmas 1980 Agnes sent presents home with me for the children that included a nearly new bike her daughter, Bethany, didn't need anymore. It needed some repairs and Craig took care of it in our bedroom on Christmas Eve. Sue and I had determined that we only had $5 that we could spend on each of our children for presents that year. The rest of Christmas was provided by the Tuckers, Sue's parents, and friends. We seemed to appreciate Christmastime more when we were financially strapped.

Shortly after Christmas, we had to check Craig into the hospital. On December 30 Sue and I returned home and left Craig by himself for the night.

Personal journal entry, Tuesday, December 30, 1980:

"I received a collect phone call from Craig. It was

around 11 p. m. He didn't feel well and wanted to know when I would be coming down. I told him that I would be there by 8 a. m. the next morning unless he needed me to come sooner. He said that would be all right. As I started to say goodbye, he said, 'I love you, Dad.' I told him that I loved him, too.

"The moment I hung up, I knew he needed me now. I changed my clothes and wrote a note to Sue and left for the hospital. I got there about 12:30 a. m. I was there for about forty-five minutes sitting beside him on his bed before he awoke and saw me. When his eyes focused in on me, his frail arms thrust upward and we embraced each other and wept. I could feel his frail and feverish body against mine. He said he didn't feel good and was tired of the fight. He got his composure back and we visited for awhile and he went back to sleep. Experiences like this are hard to overcome."

Craig returned home a few days later. He tried to attend school during January but the cold weather was hard on him and he stayed home a lot. One morning, as he started for the bus stop down the road from our house, he told his mother that he didn't think he had "much longer to go (live)." What he said was hard on her. We were doing all we could to take one day at a time, but it was very difficult to do.

Craig had to return to the hospital the first week in February for more treatments as his fever became alarmingly high again. He seemed to have a constant temperature of around 100 degrees and when it got higher and wouldn't come back down, that meant he needed to be hospitalized.

We had an interesting experience while he was in the hospital this time. His roommate, who was about the same age as Craig, was recovering from a drug overdose that he and his brother had experienced in their home while the parents were away. His older brother wasn't as fortunate and died. The family had just dropped off the clothes at the funeral home to dress the dead brother in before they came to the hospital. It was an eye-opening experience to witness the conversation of a family who didn't have the same deep feelings we had as to the eternal potential and blessings of a family. Their talk was irreverent and completely lacking in feeling. They made humorous remarks about how the brother died. Even though Craig was very weak, he picked up on what was being said and told me, "I am so thankful for the family I have and to know that I am loved."

Craig returned home during the second week of February and I talked him into going on a business trip with me to Lexington, Kentucky. The Tucker's offered me the use of their car. It would be our last trip together. The ride was hard on him but he was happy to be with his dad. We were gone for four days and after our return home, his condition continued to deteriorate.

Friday, February 27, 1981:

"Today marks the anniversary of my grandfather's (Charles Alexander) death thirty-nine years ago. He died five days after I was born. Mom couldn't go to his funeral as she was in the hospital recovering from giving birth to me. The last thing he acknowledged on the day I was born was that he was happy to know that I was named after him and that mom was doing fine. He lapsed into a coma and never regained consciousness. He died in the hospital in Jackson, Wyoming, while mom was in the hospital with me in Rock Springs.

"Craig went to school all day. (This was his last day at school.). He told his mother that he was so weak at school that his fingers shook when he held his pencil."

Saturday, February 28:

"Early this morning I had a meeting with the family in our bedroom while Craig slept. I discussed his conditions with them and asked them to participate in a family fast (a period of not eating for two meals while devoting more time to spiritual thinking to receive strength). At noon, we began our fast with prayer that included a request from Craig that he wants to be prepared for whatever Heavenly Father has in store for him. In the evening, I had to help Craig upstairs to his room and stayed with him all night. He, at times, is so weak."

Sunday, March 1:

"We went to Church this morning. Craig was able to get dressed to go. We were all waiting in the car for him. He walked out of the front door with his dark brown suit, white shirt, and brown tie on. He looked so handsome but was very weak as he steadied himself, as he walked, with his hand on the side of the house. He loves Church so much. He only lasted through the first meeting. I went to check on him and found him sitting on a table at the back of the room. He said he didn't think he could make it any further. I hugged him as he buried his head on my chest. He is so weak. Mom drove us home so he could get on oxygen. He is very sick.

"Right after noon, and before the family returned from Church, I stood outside Craig's bedroom door and overheard him praying to his Heavenly Father telling him that he can't last much longer and to bless him, along with Mom, Dad, and the family, that he will be prepared for whatever the Lord wants of him. It nearly broke my heart as I listened. He was more concerned for his family than he was for himself. I glanced around the corner of the door to find him kneeling on his bed with his eyes closed. He was too weak to get out of it. I had to get away to where I couldn't hear him and I sobbed. During the night, I gave him a father's blessing for comfort."

Monday, March 2:

"Sue and I spent last night caring for Craig. His best friend, Adam, stayed with him all night, too. Adam laid on an Army cot at the foot of Craig's bed. I spent the entire day at home to help Sue care for him. It is obvious that Craig is very critical. Prior to our family home evening tonight, I brought his little oxygen machine downstairs to the living room so he could be with the family. He really enjoyed that."

Tuesday, March 3:

"I spent last night with Craig in his room. He developed the dry heaves and was very nervous, upset, and sick. I called Dr. Burry this morning to report the dry heaves condition. He said they can do something for that as he is probably dehydrated. We made quick preparations to drive to the hospital. I called the state highway patrol to inform them that I was going to break the speed limit on my drive sixty miles to the hospital in Kansas City. They said they couldn't give me permission to break the law but would radio the officers on duty of the problem. I gave them the make and license number of our car. We took off at a high rate of speed. I kept the flashers on and drove 80-90 miles per hour on the interstate. We arrived safely about noon. Craig was put in room 523 North. Sue, the doctors, and staff were with Craig when he had a bad spell and he said he wanted me. When I walked into his room, the doctors and staff backed away while I comforted him. He loves and needs his dad. He held my hand tightly for a while.

"Carrie found out at school that we had taken Craig to the hospital and called Mom to come and get her out of school. The children are very loving and concerned about their brother. Early in the evening I drove home. I am extremely tired. Sue is staying the night with Craig. When I got home, I gathered the children around me and reported on Craig's condition. We had a family prayer to give thanks and to pray for our son and brother."

Wednesday, March 4:

"I slept like a log last night. I had Charlene sleep with me. I took Charlene and Camille to stay the day with Mom. On our way over, Camille told me, 'Daddy, I spit up some mucus today.' I know she is very worried and concerned as she knows that she has the same disease that her brother has - - the little angel. I then drove to the hospital and visited with Dr. Burry. He is very discouraged, as was his staff, as they are losing the battle with Craig. Craig was a little worse today.

"Sue left for home this afternoon while I am staying the night with Craig. Several of his friends came to visit him this evening. Carrie rode along and brought a poem that my sister, Sandy, had composed about Craig and Camille. He read it and was very pleased."

Thursday, March 5:

"Craig seemed to have a better night. This morning I got some rubbing alcohol from the nurses and rubbed down his back several times. It made him feel better. I noticed his backbone and ribs, oh, how they protrude. I have never blamed myself or Sue for Craig's and Camille's disease but do find myself wishing, from time to time, that I could have given them better bodies. This is in the Lord's hands. Craig told me that he wants to go home as he isn't getting any better. He had good and bad spells throughout the day. Sue came and spent the day with us and left for home at 6 p. m. Afterwards, I visited with the resident physician and told him that we will take Craig home Saturday morning unless he shows marked improvement. Dad called tonight and expressed discouragement over our situation. I know it has to be hard for grandparents to sit by and watch a grandchild suffer so. It has to be doubly hard for them as Mom is struggling with terminal cancer. I will stay the night with Craig."

Chapter 10

Personal journal entry, Friday, March 6, 1981:

"Craig had a very rough night. When the physical therapist came in about 3 a. m. to give him his postural drainage exercises, I told him that he has had enough - - no more pounding on his body. His chest (lungs) were tightening on him. He whimpered and cried. I reassured him of his importance to the family and tried to explain and reassure him of the tremendous joy he will ultimately have as a result of his withstanding and fighting for every breath. I told him that I loved him and that we were taking him home Saturday morning. He seemed to calm down and go to sleep at about 5:30 a. m. His poor little body has taken so much. I never knew the responsibilities of fatherhood would be so demanding. Oh, how I love my children and wife and hate to sit by and watch anyone of them suffer so! But, experiencing this has brought about a deeper and profound love for all.

"At 7:17 a. m., Sue called. I told her we are bringing Craig home tomorrow and for her to get some help to have his bed brought down to the livingroom so we can take care of him as a family. I then left the room to go to the cafeteria in the basement to get a quick bite to eat. I wasn't gone very long. When I returned, Craig was sitting up in bed with tears coming down his cheeks. I understood instantly what his need was and said questioningly, 'You don't want me to leave you, do you?' He nodded his head, 'Yes.' I sat sown beside him and hugged him. Oh, how I love my first-born! I felt a need to visit with the doctors and asked Craig if it would be all right for me to step out in the hall outside his room to visit with them. He said it would be okay. I told the doctors to make preparations now for our trip home. I am taking Craig to his family. I felt that they have done all that they can do. I went back to Craig's room and told him we are going home today and went to sit in the chair by the window. I just pondered as Craig laid there struggling for breath. Dr. Burry came at 8:40 and looked at Craig and said that he needs to be home. I knew I was making a decision that would shorten his life. The feelings I experienced were extremely heavy. There is no way that I can explain the way I felt at that moment. As I was in deep thought, Sue walked in the room at 11:30. She took a look at Craig and broke down crying. She knew something was going on. She instantly went to Craig and embraced him. I will never forget his left arm, which was taped to an IV board, as he put it around his mother and on her back as he sweetly said, 'I'm going to be all right now,' as he kept patting her on the back. Sometime in those deep moments that the both of us were experiencing, and before his mother arrived, the Spirit of the Lord offered him the comfort he had asked his Heavenly Father for that initiated his preparation and understanding that his suffering was nearing an end. Sue comforted him for sometime, or rather, received comfort from Craig. I just sat there and tried to come to an understanding of what I was feeling.

"At noon, Dr. Burry came into the room and walked to Craig's bedside. He looked down at him as tears welled up in his eyes. Craig looked up at him. No words were exchanged as Dr. Burry extended his hand to Craig and they shook hands reverently. Dr. Burry then turned, walked rapidly to the door and slapped the door casing as he left the room. Craig raised his arm in a waving gesture and sweetly said, 'Goodbye.' That was the only word that was said during the whole final scene between them. Dr. Burry had taken care of Craig for twelve years and knew that this would be the last time he would see him alive. He felt he had lost the battle. It was a very sad and extremely emotional moment.

"We waited for medications we needed to take home with us, including a tank of oxygen. It was taking a lot longer than was necessary and Craig was failing fast. At 12:30 p. m., he asked, 'Dad, would you give me a blessing so I can make it home to be with my family and tell them goodbye.' That was the heaviest moment to date in my life which had been filled with extremely heavy moments the past few months. It was very hard for me as I placed my hands on his feverish head and gave him a blessing, '... in the name of Jesus Christ and by the authority that I hold, I bless you that you will be able to make it home to be with your family.' That is all I had the emotional stamina to say.

"At 1:30, we were finally in the car and left the hospital for home. Craig was laying on the back seat breathing oxygen. We got off the interstate in Claycomo and stopped at McDonald's for something to eat. Craig ate a hamburger, fries, chocolate milk shake, and a Butterfinger candy bar. It was his first meal in days. All he ate in the hospital was a small box of breakfast cereal on Wednesday or Thursday morning. It gave me new courage. Stopping to eat also caused a serious problem as we ran out of oxygen at the Wallace State Park exit. I drove fast down rural roads for ten miles to our home. By the time we got there, Craig was unconscious. I picked him up and hurriedly carried him upstairs to his bedroom at the top of the stairs and put him on his little oxygen machine. We arrived home at 3 p. m. The oxygen revived him by the time the rest of the children arrived home from school. We had him laying on several pillows propped up in his bed. He wanted to talk to them with what strength he had left. We had a very emotional time as a family. Marcus came out of the bedroom crying his little heart out as he said, 'I want to take Craig's disease on myself so he can live! I hate Satan!' I hugged and comforted him tightly and told him how much I loved him and that this situation wasn't caused by Satan. When Craig talked to Camille, he told her to, 'Be strong; I will always be with you.'

"Late in the afternoon, Mom and Dad came out with a large bucket of Kentucky Fried Chicken for our supper. It was an emotional time as I watched my parents talk to Craig. He had his eyes closed most all of the time as he is too weak to open them and he speaks in very short sentences because of being so weak and fighting for breath. I asked the family to gather around Craig's bed and softly consider what we could do for him. It was whispered by one of the children that we have a family prayer and ask Heavenly Father to bless him. We went down stairs to the living room so as to not disturb Craig. Carrie and I went back up to his room to find him trying to sit up and pray to the Lord. He was too weak to sit up and it broke my heart to see him struggling to pray and not be able to. I wept with Carrie. Carrie and Marcus have been so helpful to Craig. After our family prayer and Craig's attempt to pray, Sue and I felt there was a sweet and calming spirit settle in our home.

"Dad and Mom stayed the night in our bed as Sue and I cared for Craig through the night. We told the family to get some sleep and we would wake them if there was a change in Craig's condition. Near midnight, he weakly asked, 'What day is it?' I told him it was almost Saturday. He was very weak, and as he gasped for breath, said, 'I don't want it to be tomorrow.' We realized he wanted to die before midnight and not make it to Saturday because it was Carrie's fifteenth birthday and he did not want to pass away on her birthday that she should always remember sadness when he wanted her to have joy. He did make it to Saturday and the battle was on for him to live another twenty-four hours."

Saturday, March 7:

"Sue and I cared for Craig all night. Neither of us slept. How could we when our beloved son suffers so and is near death. This morning, Craig had the strength to tell Carrie happy birthday and for her to have a party. He stayed the same throughout the day. He laid in his bed with his eyes closed while fighting for every breath. We tried to get him to eat some broth but he was too weak. We found that he would suck on a wet rag, so we soaked the end of a cloth in liquid Jell-O and got him to take some. We were caring for him every minute of the day as we knew that he wanted to make it past Carrie's birthday. I have never seen an example of courage like this in my entire life, nor do I expect that I ever will. Craig is breathing for another twenty-four hours with lungs damaged beyond the capacity to perform and all this for his sister and family. He has felt the tugs of eternity and wants to go on so strongly, but, he continues to fight for his family. Tears are streaming down my face as I write and try to understand a sacrifice of this magnitude. I will have to go into eternity myself before I will ever be able to understand what Craig is doing for us."

Sunday, March 8: "Our beloved son passes away."

"As the clock struck midnight, I told Craig in his ear that he did it, that he made it to Sunday - - his favorite day! I said to him, 'Let's fight till next Sunday.' He weakly asked, 'Why?' I said, 'Next Saturday you will be sixteen years old and will be able to get a drivers license.' He said, 'It doesn't really matter now, Dad.' I will always remember his response because, up until this past Wednesday, he talked about getting his drivers license. He was now committed to eternity. He asked me to give him another blessing. He asked to be blessed that his painful headaches would go away and he wanted to know what Heavenly Father wanted him to do.

"At 2:15 a. m., he started to lose consciousness and said with what voice he had left that he wanted to die now. He asked me several times to turn off his oxygen machine. I refused and told him that as long as there was one more breath to take, that he must take it for only the Lord could determine when his time on Earth was over. I went on to tell him that there will be special blessings for him in eternity when he fights. He now was unconscious but would faintly move his head when I spoke in his ear. I talked softly in his ear from 2:15 to 5 a. m. when he became conscious and weakly alert. When he became more conscious, I asked him in his ear if he loved the Lord. I will never forget his weak and determined response. He said, 'With all my heart!' I told him, 'I love you, son.' He said, 'I love you, too, Dad.' His attitude had changed during the past little while. Although he was too weak to open his eyes and talk at any length, he was at total peace. I felt that he may overcome this crisis. I was concerned but happy.

"About 7 a. m., I walked down the gentle hill behind our house about 200 yards to a grove of trees and knelt down and poured my heart out in prayer to my Heavenly Father pleading for my son's life to be spared. When I finished my prayer, I started back to the house with a peaceful feeling that I interpreted that 'all will be well.' I felt that my son would make it. I found out later in the day that Craig would be blessed to make it but not in the way that I had hoped he would.

"As I was returning to the house, Marcus was walking towards me to see if I was all right. I told him that I was and that Craig would be too. During the morning, I picked him up out of his bed and laid him on the cot at the foot of his bed and his mother washed his hair and gave him a sponge bath. He had such a happy and pain-free feeling though he constantly struggled for each breath.

"Carrie, Marcus, Christie, and Charlene were taken to Church by friends, then to their house for dinner. At 3 p. m., I thought that Craig was going to be all right and felt that I could lay down for a nap. Dad watched Craig for me while I fell into a deep sleep. At 5 p. m., Dad woke me up to let me know that Craig was failing fast. I rushed to his bedside and started to talk into his ear as I had done during the night. He tried once to move his head towards my voice but that was all he could do. We stayed with him until the end when his heart stopped at 5:42. I was dumfounded for I had felt that he would make it. The Lord let me know earlier this morning that he would be all right but not in the way that I assumed he would. My prayers have been answered but in the way the Lord wanted them to be. All those in the bedroom were quietly crying except me. I was overwhelmed with wanting to know what I was to do now. I had never been hit so hard emotionally like this before with the realization that there is a power that presides over all mortality and we are just guests on the earth. For the first time, I felt totally powerless. For fourteen and a half years I had lived Craig's death, but I was totally unprepared for it when it actually happened.

"When our son died, I had his head cradled in my left arm with my right hand on his heart; I felt its last beat. Sue was on his left side holding his left hand. Dad was on his right side holding his other hand. Mom sat on the cot with Camille on her lap. After he passed away, I removed the oxygen mask from his face. Camille came over to me and picked up the mask and put it up to her angelic face and, with little droplets of tears on her cheeks, said, 'When my disease gets as bad as Craigie's, I'll be the next one to die.' What she said shot through my heart like a hot sword. It was a hard time for all of us. Most had left the little bedroom when, all of a sudden, we heard this outburst of sobbing with a mournful cry. I went to the top of the stairs to find our Camille sitting on the second step from the bottom just sobbing her little heart out. I ran down the steps to her and held her in my arms to comfort her. It was a sad and tender moment. I called our friends who had our other children to tell them that Craig had died but they were already on their way home. When they arrived, Sue and I met them at the door and I will never forget the look on their faces when we told them that their brother was gone. Marcus and Christie ran for Craig's bedroom in disbelief. Carrie collapsed to the floor in tears. We spent some time giving them comfort as we looked at Craig's body lying so peacefully on his bed. It was a shock to my sweet children. Charlene was really too young to understand what happened.

"I called Dr. Burry at his home early this evening to let him know that Craig had passed away. He was deeply saddened when he heard the news but was expecting it sometime this weekend. I invited him to attend the funeral but he refused saying he has a policy to never attend any of the children's funerals as it is too hard on him. He went on to say how much he was impressed with our family and the manner in which we took responsibility for Craig. He said that in all the years that he has been a doctor and treating children, he has never had a situation where the father demonstrated responsibility for his child and wanted the child home to die. He said that, in most cases, the family has left the final days and hours of a child's life up to the medical staff. He went on to say that he and his staff have been, at times, the only ones to be with a child when it died. I said that I would never be able to understand that level of irresponsibility. I told him that I am Craig's father and am responsible for him from his birth to his death. He thanked me several times in our visit for my help.

"I called the funeral director and he and his son came out to get Craig's body at about 7:30. They reverently wrapped his body in a heavy dull green blanket and carried it down the stairs to the stretcher and out to the coach.

"Several friends came by to pay their respects. I made and received many phone calls. Sue is unable to get in touch with her parents as they are on the road driving here from Texas. We will just have to wait until they call to let them know that Craig is dead.

"It has been a numbing day and I feel so lost this evening without my boy. We were together so much. I know he is not suffering now and it is such a wonderful blessing, but, I miss him so much. This is a new experience for me and my family. This evening, I wonder if I will ever get over the feeling of emptiness that I have."

Chapter 11

During the last few days of Craig's life, I found myself locked into the moment of each thing that happened. I don't recall a moment where I wished that I had never had this experience or blamed myself or my sweetheart for causing Craig to suffer and die. I seemed to be controlled or not allowed to escape into a fantasy or dream world and that I was being blessed to experience the "bread of today" taught by the Savior in the Lord's prayer. I have found over the years that, from not being able to escape from the moment, it made it possible for me to feel all the depth that was important for me to feel. Each second that passed is forever imbedded in my soul, and the end result has been that I have gained a deep and profound understanding of the suffering of others and the need that I have to be involved - - especially those situations where a life is coming to an end.

Personal journal entry, Monday, March 9, 1981:

"I had a sleepless night. This is the first time in my life that my emotional hurts are centered in the heart area of my chest. Perhaps this is what a 'heartache' really feels like. We took Craig's Sunday clothes to the funeral home, and at the same time, picked out a casket. There wasn't a 3/4 size casket in the inventory and I didn't see a problem with using a full size one. A friend took the little girls to her home and had them help bake cookies. During the day, I just moped around the house and made a couple of visits to Craig's bedroom. I was disappointed that a friend had made up his bed while we were gone into town.

"Sue's mother called this morning from a motel in Waco, Texas, and literally came to pieces when Sue told her that Craig was gone.

"Later in the afternoon, I was sitting in the living-room pondering and holding the tears back when Sue remembered something and came from the kitchen to tell me. She said that Craig had been working on a lamp in wood shop as a birthday present for me but had not finished it but wanted to get it done for Father's Day. That was the reason he kept going to school when he felt so sick - - it was to finish the lamp. He never got it completed. (Craig's classmate and friend, David Dial, took it upon himself to finish turning the lamp on the school lathe and presented it to me as a special surprise in May, 1981.) That was all I needed to hear as I broke out in a sob and cried for sometime. I want my son back! Camille and Charlene were now back home, and out of instinct, climbed up on my lap and gave me hugs and kisses - - more than usual. It helped me greatly.

"Family home evening was a very sad time this evening. All we could do was to sit around, visit, cry, and sing the song, 'There is Beauty All Around When There is Love at Home.' At 10:30 p. m., Sue's parents arrived for a tearful reunion. They are staying the night with us."

Tuesday, March 10:

"I stayed home all day. Early in the evening, I was getting ready for Craig's viewing and was putting on my tie when Christie came up to me with excitement in her eyes and said, 'Craigie's not dead where he is at. He is just dead from us. We're kinda dead from Heavenly Father, too.' The sweet little angel, she is thinking deep on her own trying to understand what has happened to her brother.

"...I was overwhelmed by the out-pouring of support that we received from the community. The viewing started at 7:30 and lasted for about one and one half hours. Marcus would greet people at the door and say, 'I will show you my brother' and lead them to the casket. Christie's and Camille's school teachers brought them some ceramic dolls as presents. It was so sweet of them to do that."

Wednesday, March 11: "Our beloved son is laid to rest."

"...Craig's funeral was held forty miles away in Liberty, Missouri, where our Church had a larger building, and where we used to live many years ago. ...After the funeral, we returned to Cameron for a grave-side service. We then went to our local Church for a family meal while Craig's grave was closed. After the dinner, Sue's parents and family members drove our children home.

"...A little later, Sue and I started for home, and on the way, stopped by the cemetery to see Craig's grave for the first time. It was dark now, with only a faint line of light on the western horizon. The cemetery owner was locking the gate. He was willing to leave the gate unlocked for us to drive in, but we told him to leave it locked and he wouldn't have to return to lock it up later. We could walk in from the entrance. He gave us a flashlight to use as it was that dark now. I will never forget the emotions I had as the light from the little flashlight fell on the mound of flowers, then to the metal name plate with Craig's name, birth, and death dates on it. I gulped with emotion and embraced Sue. I seemed to feel that this is all that is left of sixteen years with our son - - a mound of flowers and a metal plate! It was overpowering as we dropped to our knees at the head of his grave and I pleaded with the Lord in prayer for strength and understanding. We walked back through the dark cemetery, forever-changed.

"As we drove up to our house, we noticed that there

were no lights on but our family's cars were parked in front. We walked in to find all sitting in the dark. I checked the circuit-breaker box on the back porch to find it in order. I went out to the meter on the light pole in the backyard and found it gone with a note attached from the power company saying they had disconnected our electricity for non-payment of our bill. The time of disconnect was 3 p. m., the same time we were sitting in our son's funeral. Our electricity comes from a rural co-op and we have to read our own meters. I completely forgot to read our meter during Craig's illness and death. I called the local representative in a neighboring town and told him of our family's problems. He asked, 'Was that your son that died that was announced on the radio station this morning?' I said, 'Yes.' He said, 'I'm sorry, Mr. Allen, but you will still have to pay the reconnect charge of $50 to get your electricity turned back on.' I will never forget those words as long as I live. Where was his empathy, or even sympathy. I asked him to come as quick as he could. I then lit our Coleman camp lantern for my family downstairs and went upstairs to Craig's bedroom and laid down on his bed and stared up in the dark wondering just how much more humiliating can life get. I am trying to eek out a living by being self-employed and, at the same time, trying to prepare myself and family, including Craig, for his passing. I have taken my wife and family through great trials and now this. It seemed to be the final act to 'grind my inadequacies and short-comings in my face.' I will have to admit that this final experience of the day broke me. I truly felt defeated and really didn't care what happened next. It was the first time in all the years of my life that I have ever felt that way. I felt like there was no use to even take another breath.

"The power company did come out and turn our lights back on and I made a check out for $81.92 which included the $50 reconnect fee. Sue's aunt left with her grandmother for Iowa while Sue's parents stayed another night with us. Oh, how I miss my son at this moment!"

Thursday, March 12:

"I stayed close to home all day with one exception when I drove to the cemetery and I will long remember as I drove west up the hill on old 36 Highway and first saw the mound of flowers off in the distance that marked my son's grave. I cannot begin to express the emotions I had as I looked at it as I drove towards the cemetery. I spent some time at his grave. The weather has been just wonderful for such a sad time. There has been only sunny and cool days for a long time, which I feel is a special blessing for us.

"When our neighbor, Faye Walker, found out what happened with the electric company last night, she made phone calls to the local board of directors then to the main office letting them know that if they don't want this despicable act of insensitivity published in the paper, they had better return the $50 reconnect fee to the Allens. Her act in our defense really helped me to get my courage back. What would life be without friends. (The power company did return our reconnect fee as a result of Faye's efforts.)

"In the mail today was a card and check from my Aunt Helen in Wyoming. The check was for $2,000! We were overwhelmed! It will pay for all the funeral expenses. Oh, how I love her. When I called her to thank her, she told me that she knew we didn't have any money and that the funeral expenses would be about that amount. She lived near us when we had our difficult times when we lived in Wyoming and has always been interested and caring for us through all that we have experienced. Oh, how we love her. (With all the contributions that we received from friends and family, including the gift from my aunt, we received enough to pay nearly all the funeral and cemetery costs. All we had to come up with was less than $11.)"

Saturday, March 14:

"Today would have been Craig's sixteenth birthday. This is a terrible way to have to celebrate it. I took the kids by the cemetery and took pictures of the grave site. The Tuckers came up for a visit this afternoon. Oh, how we love them."

* * *

A few days before Craig's passing, I received a letter

from a good friend where I was raised as a youth. She and her husband were a little older than my parents and had challenging times with the death of two of their sons. I had called her to ask if she could give me some courage during this time. She responded with a wonderful letter. In it, she told me that I would experience extremely high peaks and corresponding low points which, emotionally, would be very deep and lonely. She told me that our souls would be stretched in ways we never thought possible. She said that, over time, there would be a settling and we would be at peace with the understanding that we could go forward with our lives. I really appreciated her counsel and have found that all she had said was true.

One of the most difficult memories that I had of my son immediately after his death was of the two years we were home teaching companions and made monthly visits to several assigned families in our ward. I will never forget the way Craig was dressed, always in his suit pants, white dress shirt and tie, and his thick fluffy hair neatly in place. He loved to go home teaching with me. I asked the Bishop for the privilege of having my son as a companion. This is one of my most cherished memories that I have of Craig.

I found that for the first several weeks, even months after my son's passing, most of my emotions were in the abyss. There were good times, too, that were mostly provided by extended family and friends. I have found that each person adjusts to an experience like this in different ways and at different times. Even within a close family, there is a different timetable for each one. A couple of months after Craig's passing, my father had a conversation with a business acquaintance who had visited with Craig in December before he died and said that, "...he (Craig) told him that he wasn't afraid to die and that he didn't have long to live. He said that he was concerned about how his dad and mom would take his passing. He felt that his dad would have a rough time."

The concern that Craig had for me turned out to be true. Each member of my family worked through the experience in their own way and each of us needed to be considerate of what each other was experiencing. We needed to be patient with each other. I knew I had to go forward but found myself marking each significant event, such as, the first twenty-four hours since his death, his first birthday (six days later), the first week, month, first snow fall on his grave, etc. A very difficult time was the first Christmas. Something that I was not prepared for was when our Church directory came out with Craig's name missing from our family. I was not prepared for the emotions that came with that experience. Carrie was now listed as our first child. The little details that became major concerns or barriers to work through were not anything that I could prepare for - - they had to be lived. I found that through these experiences, my soul and heart truly was being stretched to new limits that seemed to be propelling me to an increased feeling for members of my family. My feelings for all people seemed to be intensifying.

Another experience that was difficult to accept was

when I got the final hospital bill for Craig's illness. I opened it and felt my heart sink. It had a very large sum that was owed, but what got to me was the feeling that I had when I saw this enormous bill to pay and no son to show for it. It was another challenge that had to be worked through, and with the passing of time, was conquered. The Missouri Crippled Children's Association ultimately paid the account for us.

A couple of days after Craig's passing, Marcus came down from upstairs wearing Craig's baseball hat, shirt, and belt. He was doing all he could to replace his brother and help to make his parents and sisters feel better. It was a sweet and emotional experience. It demonstrated the fact that each of us had to work through the tough time in our own personal ways.

There were times when I had to take a walk out into the fields and timber near our home to think and to work through emotional downturns. One time I walked to the bridge over Shoal Creek a half a mile north of our house, and sat under the north end experiencing deep sorrow. I was hoping the bridge would collapse on me to end it all. Even though I felt this way, it seemed to be a surface feeling, because down deep, I knew that I needed to go on with each day. There was an inner feeling telling me that it was all right to experience the feelings that I was, and that there was more to life than sorrows. As I worked through the surface sorrows, it seemed to give strength to my inner sole.

Not long after Craig died, a friend of ours told us of a special experience she and her daughter had while visiting with my family during the Christmas holidays before his passing. They wanted to check in and see how we were doing - - especially Craig - - and to drop off some candy. As they were leaving, they remarked to each other of the special feeling they both had while in our home. They said it was such an angelic environment they had experienced that they stopped their car on the next little hill about 200 yards from our home to look back to see if there was any heavenly glow about it. They said that the feeling in our home was that strong and sweet. It was interesting how others could sense a special feeling when they were with us but all that I could feel was sadness. I knew that we were being blessed and cared for but I was not yet to the point where I could feel that we were.

A couple of months after Craig's passing, as I was out working for the day and Sue was at home with Charlene, there was a knock at the front door. It was our friend, Emma Emmett, with a single red rose in a vase that she gave to Sue. She told Sue that she didn't understand the experience she was having as a mother who just lost a child, but she was thinking of her that morning and felt that she needed to do something that demonstrated her concern. We will always remember the rose and the interest Emma had in driving eleven miles out into the country to deliver it with her love. A wise man said: "The Lord almost always answers our prayers through people."

The first Christmas after Craig's death was a very

difficult time for me and my family. The Methodist Church in our community voted to have our family as the family they wanted to provide Christmas for. On Christmas Eve, there was a knock at our door, and as we opened it, we discovered the Watkins family with their arms full of presents and food. We wept with gratitude in our hearts for the kindness that had been shown to us by so many of our friends in the community. Religious differences know no bounds when we follow our inner feelings that promote Christlike acts of service.

There were many special and sacred experiences within our family that we had following Craig's passing that I have recorded in my personal journal. These cherished experiences will remain private. However, it might be appropriate to share one that happened during the month following his death.

Tuesday, April 21:

"Sue woke up at about 2 a. m. and spent sometime crying. She kept saying over and over that she can't bear giving up Camille when it comes time for her to die. Charlene had crawled in bed with us sometime during the night and was laying between Sue and me sound asleep when she said, 'Mommy, you don't have to give up Camille.' I picked up her hand and it was completely limp. She was still in a sound sleep. We believe that this sweet experience was given to us by the Lord through our precious child. It brought peace and comfort to both of us and Sue was able to fall asleep."

Chapter 12

One of the most memorable and sweetest experiences that I have ever had was when Sue came to me in May following Craig's passing and embraced me as she said, "I would like for us to have a baby son, I want you to have another companion." She was very sensitive to what I had been feeling and wanted me to be not so lonely. She knew very well that she still had to nurture Camille through her life, along with our other children, and that she was opening herself up for the potential of having another child with Cystic Fibrosis. Oh, how I appreciated her feelings of love and the tremendous sacrifice that she was willing to accept for me. However, no more children came to our home. Charlene was our last and we feel so blessed to have the six children that we did. Each one of them has provided special strengths and support through the years. They have been a true joy to us.

In the months following our experiences with Craig, I had a hard time working in the shop as Craig spent a lot of time sitting and watching me work when he was too sick to go to school. Those memories were too painful for me and I felt a need to get into another field of work. I tried selling insurance for several years, and after the first two years, was able to bring a consistent income home. The main thing I learned was that not all of society was experiencing economic problems like we had.

During this time, my folks lost the wood shop and equipment. They turned everything over to the bank to be auctioned off to satisfy debt. My parents left town in their car, towing a small rental trailer that contained their clothes and some hand tools. They moved to Colorado to live with my sister and her family to take care of her while she struggled with cancer. My sister had moved there from Cameron two or three years earlier. Mom was still able to help my sister a little while suffering with her own illness. Dad told me of a very difficult experience he had when he came home one day and found Mom crawling on her hands and knees up the short stairway to their bedroom, weak, and in pain. She had helped my sister in the living room on a lower level as she, too, was gravely ill. Mom did all that she could for her and was trying to get back to her own bedroom but was too weak and in great pain when Dad found her. Her heart was full of love and the desire to help even when she was struggling with her own terminal illness. My parents continued to show their love and determination to sacrifice for their family after their move West. Dad built a cabinet for a client and earned $135 as his profit after expenses. For

Christmas, Mom sent us a check for $90 and sent one for $45 to a younger sister and her family, who were also struggling. They kept nothing for themselves. After suffering for several years, my mother died in 1984 and my sister a year later.

By 1985 Sue and I felt a need for me to get out of selling insurance and get back into working with wood. The decision to make the transition came about in a most interesting way. During 1984, I experienced an emotional melt-down and was hospitalized twice in a six month period while I was undergoing medical treatment. I had a rare reaction to the strong and controlling medication I had to be taking which caused a very painful intestinal obstruction. After completely recovering, I knew I had to generate some quick income because I had exhausted my meager financial reserves and the disability insurance I had with the company I was working for. The only way I knew to get quick commissions in the insurance business was to sell annuities which did not require an approval time like selling an insurance policy did. Annuities are ways to invest in insurance companies. I decided to call my brother who was living and working in Bolivia, South America, supervising construction on several building projects for our Church. I asked him if he knew of anyone who lived there who would be interested in investing in annuities offered by American insurance companies. I felt that people in a foreign country would be more eager to have a "piece of America" than those who lived in the United States. My brother felt that there could be many he knew that would be interested. We made the necessary arrangements for me to be gone three weeks and my brother paid for my airline ticket as I had very little money of my own. My bank account held $51.69 and I withdrew $50 to make the trip, leaving my wife with $1.69. We planned for her to have a garage sale while I was gone. With what food and fuel we had on hand added to what she could sell, we determined she should be able to make it.

The night before I flew to La Paz, Bolivia, we had our weekly family home evening where I explained to my family why I needed to make the trip. While I was talking to my children, Charlene, who was seven years old at the time, had been sitting on my lap when she jumped down and ran to her bedroom. She quickly returned with a nickel in her hand. It was all the money she had and she gave it to me to help with the trip. It was an emotional time for me and I wept. I instantly recalled the Biblical parable of the widow's two mites (Mark 12:42, King James Version). I carried her nickel with me while I was in South America, and later, taped it in my journal and wrote up the story.

In the three weeks I was in Bolivia, I met with many people but never sold an annuity. I traveled with my brother for a couple of days in the Amazon basin where we checked on the mahogany windows, doors, and trim that was being made in a large woodworking plant in Santa Cruz. When I walked in the factory, I instantly smelled sawdust and walked over to a door that was on display to rub my hand over it. The construction method was similar to the historic doors I had made in the past. As I felt and inspected the door while smelling the sawdust, something in me changed in an instant and I knew I had to get back into historic window and door making.

When I arrived back home, I was concerned about what my wife would say when she would find out that I didn't sell an annuity. After I explained my selling disappointment and experience in the wood working plant, she said that she had been praying for my success and had the distinct feeling that she should encourage me to get back to working with wood. During the years since then, I marveled that I had been sick for several months and hospitalized, reduced to near-nothing financially, took a trip to South America paid for by a loving brother, found myself in the Bolivian interior where I smelled sawdust and felt a door. I needed these experiences so I could be turned back to working with wood. It is a marvelous thing when we consider the path the Lord leads us on to accomplish what he has in store for us if we stay the course. It is hard for God to direct our footsteps if we are not moving in some direction on our own using our free-agency and conscience to guide us.

I made the transition and have been self-employed in historical window and door work ever since.

A couple of years after Craig's death, I was called to serve as Bishop of our ward (local Church congregation).

I was quick to find out that, over a relatively short period of time, several of our members were diagnosed with terminal illnesses. I found myself deeply involved with critical situations. One situation involved the illness and death of a husband and father of three children. He died on the night before Christmas Eve. His funeral was held the day after Christmas. Less than a week later, I made a visit to the home to see how things were working out as I had assigned a family in our ward to take the grieving family under their wing. They made sure they had what was needed as to emotional comfort and friendship and I took care of their basic financial needs from Church funds as they were needed. During my visit, I found happiness and laughter. I was surprised with what I observed as there was no happiness, joy, or laughter in my life following Craig's death. As the mother walked with me to the door at the conclusion of my visit, I remarked of the happiness and laughter I saw. She told me that they were able to accept what had happened, and to make the adjustments they did because of my involvement with them, to include, being there when her husband died. During the crisis, I was able to explain why they were feeling the way they did and how they were going to next feel. It was a great comfort to her that she personally knew someone who had recently made it through a similar experience.

On my eight mile drive home, I was very discouraged, and somewhat angry that I had to go through what I did so that others could be happy. It was a disappointing experience for me but I couldn't help to keep from feeling that way. By the time I got home, I had worked myself out of those feelings and realized that it was a blessing for me that I could really understand how another person felt while going through very difficult times. I came to the conclusion that I needed to be thankful for the opportunity that I had to serve others with complete understanding.

Another very important activity that has helped me for a long time has been keeping a journal of my life. I began recording my experiences about the time Charlene was born. I started recording on a daily basis during the days prior to Craig's passing. I have filled thousands of pages of my daily activities since then. Keeping a consistent journal has been a form of therapy for me. No one else in my family felt the need to keep a daily record. This is, in no way, a criticism of them as each had to work through their challenges in their own way. For me, that included keeping a detailed record of my life. Over the years that I have been keeping a journal, my family has expressed their appreciation for my record as they now find a need, from to time, to reconnect with the experiences of the past.

The impact that journal keeping can be was brought home to me several years ago when I was researching my ancestral family who first settled in New England in the early seventeenth century. I came across the final testimony of my eighth great grandfather, who was born in England and had served as governor of the Massachusetts

Bay Colony several times. He wrote out a testimony of his Christian feelings at the beginning of his will. At that time, it was the custom to write out a will just prior to death. Oft-times the wills were dictated as the person was dying. Governor Dudley's testimony and will were written two weeks before his death in 1653. After making a statement of his beliefs, he concluded by writing: "...leaving this testimony behind me, for the use and example of my posterity, and any other upon whom it may work." When I read those words, I had a special sensation that caused me to say out loud, "I got it!" I had received the testimony he wrote to me almost 350 years before. It was an eye-opening experience that I had as to the power and influence that we can be to direct our posterity long after we are dead. It has been my experience that we will not feel a need to keep a record of our lives if we, ourselves, don't feel that there is life beyond the grave. Why would we be interested in our posterity if we believe we will not have an eternal future ourselves? I have found that we have an inner understanding or hope that this life is not all there is to our existence. I want to do all that is within my power to leave a path of counsel for my descendants to follow. As Biblical scriptures teach us, if we are worthy, I can fully expect our family to transcend this life.

It is a known fact that small and insignificant experiences, when exposed to the passing of time, can become very significant and have major influences in our future. Benjamin Franklin wrote: "A little neglect may breed great mischief... For lack of a nail the shoe was lost; for lack of a shoe the horse was lost; for lack of a horse, the rider was lost." Neglect is lack of order. Writing a consistent record of our experiences is a wonderful way to maintain order in our lives. When we search the past, we quickly realize that all history is a compilation of daily events, which over time, and combined with future daily activities, can blossom into great things. I became aware of this fact when I continued to learn of my ancient family from New England. One of my seventh great grandfathers was Henry Dunster. He was the founding president of Harvard University. In compiling a biography on his life, I came to an understanding of how small activities and decisions can have major impact on the future.

When President Dunster organized Harvard College, he started with a handful of students and did all the teaching by himself, aided only by tutors that he had trained. Through his dedicated efforts over fourteen years, he kept the fledgling school from closing its doors. Today, Harvard is, perhaps, the most well known university in the world. In 1643 President Dunster drew up a crude shield with over-turned books and the word "Veritas" written on them to represent the young college. That particular university symbol has been seen in every country, and is by far, the most widely recognized symbol of higher learning in the world today. Finally, Dunster was expelled from the university and Colony when he took a stand against the Puritan doctrine of infant baptism by refusing to have his new-born son baptized. His act of quiet rebellion, even to the extent of giving his life, if necessary, paved the way for other religious organizations to gain a foothold that opened the way for our constitutional right of freedom of religion.

It is important for us to reach forward to our unborn generations, because some of our descendants will reach back in time to us. To be a beacon of light and influence to them, we need to leave a record of our lives which must contain more than historical facts. It must contain our thoughts, feelings, and personal and family traditions. We must come to know that we can make a difference in the future, then do something about it.

To rephrase Benjamin Franklin's philosophy: "For lack of interest a scribe was lost; for lack of a scribe the record was lost; for lack of a record the future was lost."

Chapter 13

In May 1989 we moved our family and business to Illinois. We were awarded a contract to build historic buildings in the town of Nauvoo. During the last half of the 1980s Camille's health was normal . She was a cheerleader, swimmer, basketball player, and played the french horn in the school band. Her health continued to be as normal as possible in the early 1990s. She consented to move with us to Nauvoo if she could still go to the CF clinic in Kansas City. We drove the 280 miles for her to have her checkups, which included the first time she was hospitalized in the spring of 1992. Her fever and lung infection was more than usual and required the customary tune-up. We could see that her health was starting to change. I drove to Kansas City to see Camille a couple of days after her mother had admitted her. It deeply affected me to see that she was in the same room that Craig had been in eleven years earlier when we took him home for the last time. The only difference was she was in the other bed. I mentioned this to Carol Hafeman, Dr. Burry's assistant, and she was very apologetic and was ready to change rooms. I told her that it wouldn't be necessary as I had to get over it.

The long drives to visit Camille while she was in the hospital in Kansas City convinced us that she didn't have much of an option other than to be transferred to the clinic in Peoria, Illinois. She objected at first but finally consented to the move. Her first visit to the new clinic showed her that her experiences there would be okay. Craig was always reserved and appreciable of any effort that was made in his behalf, even at the end of his life. Camille approached her challenge differently. She was feisty with all who took care of her when she was starting to be hospitalized. In fact, she was difficult during normal clinic visits. I am convinced that it was her way of dealing with her illness. By being defiant, she felt that she was in control. I believe that she acquired this determination during her first month of life as she had to have the will to stay alive while losing so much of her weight after birth.

I called her my Buttercup. When she was a year old and recovered from the very difficult challenges she had from birth, Sue and I took her to Spokane, Washington, where we spent a week to have a change of scenery. I carried her over the fields "down below the hill" where I played as a child and where my favorite flower grew in the early spring. It was the small, fragrant Buttercup. They were in bloom during our visit, and I called her Buttercup from that time on.

By the time Camille was in need of more frequent

hospitalization, three of our children were married - - Carrie in 1986, Marcus and Christie in 1992. Carrie and her husband had our only grandchild at that time. Our family was expanding without any apprehensions about the problems we had with Cystic Fibrosis. We hoped that our children would not let what happened to our family affect their outlook on life. It was our desire that they would not have fear that would keep them from experiencing all the wonderful things we had been able to have. The children learned along with Sue and I that life could be very difficult but that wasn't a reason to not go forward with it. We tried to do all that we could to teach our family that there was a positive outcome to all that we had gone through as a family We were very proud that the experiences we had never deterred our children from going forward as they (experiences) provided a foundation that they could build their future upon.

Camille graduated from high school in 1993 and was able to enter a local community college the fall before she passed away. She was even able to buy her own car. She was vibrant, quick-witted, very bright, and a joy to be around. She needed hospitalization several times during the last year of her life. We understood that her situation was getting critical and were doing the best we could to prepare for her passing. Even though we had experienced the death of a child before, this was a new experience because this was my Buttercup that was suffering. Before it was Craig. A different child brought a different set of circumstances and different emotions, and I feel, this was because we were, and had been, interacting with different personalities. Generally speaking, the experiences were similar, but specifically, there was a difference. It seemed to be the same, yet, it was different.

I began this writing by sharing our experiences during Camille's passing and I will conclude with the days immediately following her death.

Personal journal entry, Wednesday, November 23, 1994:

"I went unconscious last night. I slept as though I had been drugged. I found that Sue did not fare so well and struggled. We lay close to each other this morning, embracing and consoling. Marcus, Kathy (Marcus' wife), and Maya (our two month old granddaughter) slept in our living room to offer their support. I appreciated that. Sue, Marcus, and I spent most of the morning meeting with the funeral director in Hamilton to discuss finances and select a casket. I chose an inexpensive silver colored one very similar to Craig's. We also talked about scheduling. I asked the director what he thought of his work. He started to talk about the business. I stopped him and said, 'I am really interested in you personally,' as I pointed my finger at him for emphasis. I then said, 'Let me explain where I am coming from. This is a very emotionally sensitive time for us and I still feel a responsibility for Camille's body. I want to be able to trust the person who cares for her, and I don't know you.' The director was very surprised and somewhat shocked as I continued, 'I am here to get a feeling of you and who you are and of your sensitivity for your work and our needs.' He then explained his feelings for life, family, and children. I then said, 'I feel good about you and my apprehensions are alleviated.' By this time he had tears in his eyes and felt humble. I did not mean to be hard on him but I had to know and the Lord blessed me to be at peace.

"We spent the day receiving phone calls and having visits from wonderful friends in our Church and community."

Thursday, November 24: "Thanksgiving Day"

"I had another decent night's rest and awoke to find tears falling gently down Sue's cheeks. We consoled each-other for some time. Marcus, Kathy, and Maya stayed the night, again. I lounged around for most of the day, receiving calls and visits.

"We had a wonderful Thanksgiving dinner provided by Church members and friends. It was so kind of them. Marcus, Christie, Carrie, and Charlene put an album together of Camille's life to display at the viewing tomorrow evening. Mike (Christie's husband) and Charlene had previously matted some pictures, including paintings Camille had done. Later in the afternoon, I went on a ride in the historic district including the area by the river where Camille and I last kayaked together. Oh, how I miss her! This evening, I feel the heaviness settling upon my heart. Oh, to go into her empty bedroom!

"When we went to bed, Sue clutched the pillow Camille's head was on when she died and cried herself to sleep."

Friday, November 25:

"I awoke this morning before 6 a. m. to find Sue still clutching Camille's pillow. It was a precious sight. At 8:45, Sue, Charlene, Carrie, and I met in the living room to discuss and have a prayer before we left for Carthage to get Camille's body ready. When we arrived and were taken to the place where her body lay, I walked over and stroked Camille's head and face. I wanted the girls to know it was all right. It was a very special experience for all of us. Charlene didn't realize her body would be so hard. I took the time to talk about how important the spirit is as our spirit is who we really are. I helped lift and turn her body while the girls and Sue put her skirt and blouse on. I then sat down while Carrie fixed her hair and Charlene applied Camille's favorite make-up. To see how meticulous and caring both were and how unafraid they were was a special experience for me. Sue assisted them as needed. I would occasionally get things for Carrie from the funeral staff. It took us about an hour then we returned to Nauvoo.

"Sue's parents arrived just before noon. We had many friends and family visit with us during the day. At 2:00 p. m., we all went to the funeral home a couple blocks from our home where Camille's body had been taken for a private-time visitation with family and close friends. Carrie finished fixing Camille's hair. It was an emotional time for our family. At 7:00 p. m. we went to the viewing which lasted two hours. I didn't realize the impact that Camille's life had on so many of her classmates. We returned home for some time with family and friends and got a bite to eat."

Saturday, November 26: "Our daughter is laid to rest."

"I didn't sleep very well last night. I woke up at 3:00 a. m. and got up at 6:00. Sue was clutching Camille's pillow tightly even while she was in a deep sleep. We made preparations to leave for Church. Sue asked me to give her a special blessing for comfort and strength. I had Dad assist me.

"We arrived at Church at 8:30 a. m. where there was a short viewing time for those who were unable to attend last night. At about 9:00 we had our family prayer, which I asked Dad to give. The funeral director asked me to assist him in closing the casket. It was a blessing to me as it kept me busy during a very emotional time. We then went into the chapel for the service. Marcus was playing the organ and had organized the music for the service. He did a wonderful job. He played his personal arrangement of a special hymn which was very spiritual. Christie prepared and delivered Camille's personal history.

Every member of my family participated in some way. I had explained to Bishop Jacobs that I wanted to speak after the main speaker was finished but didn't want him to announce me as I was not completely sure that I could do it. I asked him to look at me after the main talk and I would nod 'yes' or 'no' to indicate what to do. I had a prayer for strength earlier in the morning, and when the time came, I nodded to the Bishop 'yes' that I would speak. I thanked those who were in attendance and all those who stood by and supported our family during our time of need. I then spoke of the blessings of what a relationship with the Savior would bring. I then talked to my family about never shying away from making decisions that would lead to difficult times. ...It was a difficult thing for me to do but I was glad for the opportunity.

"We then drove to Cameron, Missouri, where Camille was buried next to her brother following a grave-side service for those of our friends who live there. There were about 100 who attended. It was a special experience to be among long time friends. I spoke briefly then dedicated her grave before burial. We then went to our local Church for a meal while the grave was being closed. After eating, we returned to the cemetery to pay our respects then drove the 230 miles back home."

* * *

The goodness that we experienced from family and friends during our experiences with Craig's illness and death, continued for us during our difficulties with Camille. One of those very special experiences happened on what would have been Camille's twentieth birthday the following February 19. Sue and I returned home after work to find a vase on our dining room table with twenty tulips in it. Tulips were Camille's very favorite flower and our good friend, Debbie, had not forgotten.

Not long after Camille's death I was having an emotional struggle so went upstairs to her empty bedroom to try and feel close to her. I turned the pages of her date book where she kept a lot of her personal information. I discovered that on September 11 (a little more than two months before she died) she had made an $80 tithing payment to the Church. I looked through her checkbook and discovered that she had gross earnings for the year of $970 and had made $17 in tithing payments before she made the one for $80. That was her last payment and it was made on our thirty-first wedding anniversary. What greatly impressed me was that Camille was paying her tithing unknown to me or her mother and was a full and honest tithe payer when she died. I had the distinct impression that she was getting her things in order but none of us (including her) knew that it was in preparation for her death. I was filled with joy that one of my children understood the importance of paying tithing to the Lord and was doing it without being invited or reminded to. I then went to my office to look for things in my journals from past years that had anything to do with Camille. I found many entries that were of great interest to me. I will share a couple of them with you. One was a poem she wrote at Christmastime in 1987 when she was in the seventh grade. The students were given an assignment to write something about Christmas. Her poem was printed in the local newspaper. She wrote:

It was many, many years ago,
A boy was brought to us;
That we might worship him;
His name was Jesus.

The night was dark and chilly,
But a pretty star shone brightly down
On all the people who were resting,
In the sleeping town.

Then along came the wise men three,
And shepherds who worshiped him on bended knee.
Gifts of music, frankincense, and gold,
Were showered on him, the little King of old.

And that's the story of Christmas,
It will never die,
For He truly loves us
And left His words for us to live by.

Camille Allen

Camille was not one to exhibit a religious side to her personality and these discoveries were very comforting to me and brought peace to my heart.

The other entry that I found was somewhat of a shock. It came from my 1983 journal and was under the notation in the index, "Camille upset." I found that it happened on November 26 (the same day of the month, but eleven years before, that we held her funeral and she was buried). I quickly turned to November 22 (which also was a Tuesday, the same day of the week as well as the same date that she died) and found this entry:

Personal Journal Entry, Tuesday, November 22, 1983:

"...I didn't get home until 11:15 p. m. Camille was still awake and very frightened. Charlene was in my bed again so I made my bed on the couch and also made a bed on the cushions next to the couch for Camille to sleep on. I held her hand until she went to sleep. My heart aches for her."

Saturday, November 26, 1983:

"... As I was laying in bed tonight writing in this journal, Camille came quietly to my bedside and said she can't sleep. I put my journal and pen down and extended my arms to her. She laid on top of me with her little head buried between my neck and shoulder. I held her for a few moments and asked her if I could help. She quietly said, 'I have a problem.' I asked her what it was. She started sobbing and said she has been thinking of Craig and his death. I asked her what about it. She had been dreaming about it and she has been worried about it for the past few nights, since last Tuesday. I asked her if she is worried that she has the same disease as Craig and that he died from it. She said, as she cried her little heart out, 'Yes.' I couldn't control my emotions either as I stroked her soft thick blond hair. I asked her if she remembered what Craig told her just before he died. She said, 'No.' I reminded her that he told her to 'be strong' and that he would 'always be near' her. I told her that there have been times when he has come to her and kissed her cheek and she has not known it. I told her that, 'It won't be long and Craig will be by your side to comfort you and you will know it and you will see him and you won't be afraid to die because he will be there to help you, and your mommy and I will help you, too.'

"When I talked to Craig like this, I was philosophical with very little emotion because I was speaking of things I had heard of and assumed to be true and it is not that difficult accepting a child's death when they are still here and relatively healthy. This time, the pain was there and the emotion, too. I know that my blond haired Buttercup will be called on, which makes these words I write this evening of the experience I had with her a most precious thing. As I held her in my arms and could feel her little heart beating, I quietly wondered to myself how much longer before the courageous little heart stops and once again I must 'bow down to the dust' with the agony of separation. My heart will surely break - - the Lord's will be done. The words I write are but a hollow indication of the way I feel.

"She quieted down. It is past midnight. I went upstairs

and fixed her a bed on the cushions next to the couch and I made me a bed on the couch. Before we laid down to sleep, we had a special prayer. I held her hand until she went to sleep. Oh, how I pray the Lord will bless this precious little angel who must yet pass through greater suffering before she 'sleeps'."

Camille started getting upset and worried the evening of Tuesday, November 22, 1983, and it lasted through late Saturday, November 26. She was eight years old at the time. These experiences not only took place on the same dates that she died and was buried eleven years later, but they were on the same days of the week. I don't know what meaning, if any, this has but it was very emotional for me to look back in time and identify some special and sacred experiences like this. When I read those experiences of so many years ago, in my mind I could still feel her little heart beating against my chest as I held her tightly. It brought tears of sorrow and remembrance, yet, they were tears of peace.

The story of our family would not be complete without sharing two Christlike sacrifices offered by Camille's sister, Christie, and a very sweet friend named Eva Gubler. On a Sunday not long after we returned with Camille from her visit to the lung transplant center in St. Louis, Christie offered in her testimony during a Church service that she was willing to give one of her lungs to Camille when she is ready for a transplant. She was very emotional while she stood at the pulpit and expressed her love for her sister, family, Heavenly Father, and her desire to provide one of her lungs. The entire congregation was affected in a very deep and profound way.

The next morning, Sister Eva Gubler came into our business to talk to me. She and her husband, Mel, are from the state of Washington and were here serving a mission for The Church of Jesus Christ of Latter-day Saints who owns most of the sites and property in the historic district of Nauvoo. The older retired couples in the Church have the opportunity to volunteer their services for a year or eighteen months at their own expense while serving missions as guides in the historic district and in maintenance work on the property owned by the Church. Sister Gubler heard Christie bear her testimony the day before in Church. She said to me, "I talked it over with Mel yesterday and my lungs are old by they are good, clean, and strong and I want to give one of them to Camille when she has the transplant operation." Words can never express the feeling that penetrated my soul when I heard what she was willing to do for our daughter. As I looked into her eyes while she spoke to me, I saw tears welling up and felt that her offer to make a sacrifice of this magnitude was real. I can never explain how I felt as I witnessed for myself the offer she made to lay her life on the line for someone she was not related to and that she didn't know very well. Both she and Christie felt a need from a higher power to make the sacrificial offer with the understanding that the Lord would care for them as they did. In times of great need, the opportunity is there for us to offer our services well beyond our level of predetermined convenience. We have the opportunity to experience real growth and to understand principles of eternity.

Chapter 14

When I asked for the opportunity to speak at the conclusion of Camille's funeral, I wanted to express, in a very personal and poignant way, of the need for members of my family to not take the "path of least resistance" when they are confronted with choices. I felt that I had the opportunity to give counsel to them at a time when their hearts were open and sensitive to special understanding. I asked them to never depart from the counsel that we receive from the sacred scriptures and always make prayer a part of daily life. I reminded them that their mother and I had made a tough decision a long time ago, and that we wouldn't be at Camille's funeral that day if we hadn't made the decision to continue having children. I wanted all of my family to know that our decision was correct many years ago, that it is correct now, and it will always be the correct decision. It has been through experiencing difficult times and receiving help, support, and love from others during those times that have made us the people we are today.

I have used the word *adversity* numerous times in this book. The older I get, the more I am made aware of the value and necessity of *adversity*. We can do good to anyone in both serene or difficult times, but it has been my experience that the level of service that I am willing to do for others is determined by what I have learned from personal experiences during trials and hardship. Life seems to have an abundance of self-polishing opportunities. A lapadist (an expert in precious stones) places small rough and jagged pebbles in a tumbler with an abrasive polishing compound. The stones are allowed to tumble for many days until they become sufficiently polished by being forced to grind against each other during the tumbling action. The type of compound mixed in with the pebbles determines the brightness or luster of the finished product.

Life is so much like pebbles in a tumbler. We, like the pebbles, are thrown together in a societal tumbler of daily life. We seem to be forced to rub up against each other and inner act in the experiences that life has to offer. The polishing compound can be compared to the type of experiences we have along with the level of involvement we are willing to give. The more we are involved, the more polished and desirable, as a person, we become. If we are not involved with others and live reclusive lives, we will not have the opportunity to grow and develop in the the way that we could. When we pray for Divine guidance during troublesome times, then, after praying for help, isolate ourselves, we will never receive the help that we could be given. The Lord almost always answers our prayers through people. It is very important that we inner act with others during times of trials and difficulties.

For many years I have enjoyed doing research to find all I can about the lives of my ancient family, especially those who helped settle this nation in the seventeenth century. I have already referred to President Henry Dunster (founding president of Harvard University) and Thomas Dudley (governor of the Massachusetts Bay Colony). I have learned a great deal about *adversity* and challenges from another eighth great grandfather named Ezekiel Cheever. He taught Latin to young men in the grammar schools of New England for seventy continuous years. He began teaching when he was twenty-four years old and taught up until two weeks before his death, in 1708, at the age of ninety-four. Master Cheever had more influence over the minds of the young men of New England during this period than anyone else in our nation's history. A close, and much younger friend, Judge Samuel Sewall, recorded his last visit with Ezekiel two days before his death:

> August 19, 1708, I visited Mr. Cheever again, just before Lecture; Thank'd him for his kindness to me and mine; desired his prayers for me, my family, Boston, Salem, the Province. He rec'd me with abundance of Affection, taking me by the hand several times. He said, The Afflictions of God's people, God by

> them did as a Goldsmith, knock, knock, knock, knock, knock, knock, to finish the plate; it was to perfect them not to punish them.

Ezekiel Cheever died as he lived - - in humble circumstances, always taking the opportunity to teach the truth to eager listeners. The last advise he gave to his trusted friend, Judge Sewall, concerned adversity. He was not extolling the virtues of the goldsmith trade when explaining the numerous knocks with a hammer it took to produce a plate. He was bearing his testimony to the necessity of *adversity* in God's plan to develop children of character. According to Master Cheever, the Lord would have tried and tested followers.

We started a special family tradition the Christmas after Craig died by placing a lighted candle in a glass container on his grave. I read of this tradition that was practiced years ago in northern Europe. Family members of the deceased lit candles and placed them in the snow on their loved one's graves. It must have been a beautiful sight to see the candles flickering in the cold winter night. We continued this tradition while we lived in Missouri. Since our move to Illinois, we light the same container we used for Craig's grave and place it in an obvious place in our home. That is a small thing that we do to remember our sweet son during this time of year. Now, there are three candle containers that we light. One for Craig, one for Camille, and another one for little Camille, our sweet granddaughter who died the day she was born in 1996. The three lit candles are a reminder that our family can be eternal if we are faithful to sacred commitments that my wife and I made in a special place a long time ago.

It has been my desire that in writing the details of our family's experiences, they will help in some way to bring comfort and courage to others who may read this book. The only way I have found that I can be of help to others is to share personal and sensitive experiences that I have had. They tend to provide a basis of understanding with the sufferer before I can give comfort that is understood. As a family, we have been very willing and prepared to help where we have felt there was a need. However, it has never been our desire to advertise or promote what has happened to us. There is a fine line between sharing to give help and advertising to get attention. Attention is what we do not need. Opportunities to share, that may make a difference in someone else's life, is what we all need.

All of us have had unique experiences of one kind or another. Many times, those experiences have been learned through sorrow and a stretching effort. The more willing we have been to come to the aid of others who have been experiencing similar challenges, and to have done so without self-imposed limitations, the lighter our burdens have become. It is a natural phenomenon that while we are involved in genuine and heart-felt service to others, our problems are not as difficult.

My wife was hesitant for me to expose most sensitive experiences in this writing. After reconsidering, she, too, came to the conclusion that the only way to provide help and encouragement to those in need was to tell the whole story. Only by being willing to share what is true and dear to us can we hope to gain the trust of another. All of our children are very supportive of this effort. They, too, want the reader to know that there is happiness and growth during the trials of life. We each have the privilege to pay the price to become acquainted with God.

> To whom do we look, in days of grief and disaster, for help and consolation?... They are the men and women who have suffered, and out of their experience in suffering they bring forth the riches of their sympathy and condolences as a blessing to those now in need. Could they do this if they had not suffered themselves?
>
> ... Is not this God's purpose in causing his children to suffer? He wants them to become more like himself. God has suffered far more than man ever did or ever will, and is therefore the great source of sympathy and consolation ...
>
> *Orson F. Whitney, 1918*

Epilogue

When Camille passed away, our circumstances changed instantly, but, it took several years to settle into a routine without a consistent life-threatening concern. During the years that we cared for Craig and Camille, we had many humorous experiences typical to any family situation. Those experiences, though, seemed to always be tempered by the thought of an impending death. Nevertheless, our family had many happy and fun times. After Camille's death, we were able to shift our efforts to getting our family business stabilized. Since then, we have continued to have varied experiences with numerous opportunities to help those in need.

Our most recent sad experience was the day that little Camille was born and died. I will never forget walking into the hospital room where I saw Christie cradling, in her arms, the tiny lifeless body of her daughter that was born prematurely. Christie and Camille were close in age and very close as friends. When Christie found out that she was expecting a little daughter, it was her opportunity to memorialize her sister by naming her daughter after Camille. It was another difficult experience for our family in the spring of 1996 when we laid our little Camille in her grave.

As a child growing up, I developed an interest in the country of Iceland. It has always intrigued me. Not long ago, I arranged for my wife and me to travel there and spend a week. I will long remember Sue's expression as she opened my letter to her at Christmastime. She adjusted her glasses as she read that the letter was "good for a trip for two to Reykjavik, Iceland," the following February. It was a combination gift for Sue's birthday, our thirty-fifth wedding anniversary, her Christmas present, and Valentine's Day present. Not many people want to go to Iceland at any time, let alone in the winter. It was the least expensive place I could find to go that was outside of the United States. We had a wonderful time among sweet people. We found that Iceland is, indeed, a very unique country, and warmer than Illinois in the wintertime. When my son-in-law asked Sue what she thought of her Christmas present, her response was, "It has been one heck-of-a-ride with this guy that all started with our first honeymoon night camping at Mirror Lake in the Uinta Mountains."

* * *

Charles and Susann Allen have been married thirty-eight years and live in Nauvoo, Illinois, where they own and operate a small family business. Sue manages The Allyn (old English spelling for Allen) House tourist gift shop while Charles works in the Allyn Historic Sash Company building window sash and doors for historic restoration projects, located mostly in New England. He and his fellow workers recently completed building the windows and front doors for the rebuilding of the historic Nauvoo Temple for The Church of Jesus Christ of Latter-day Saints. Although a crew of six to seven men were used during much of the thirty-four months of working on the temple, things have returned to normal with a two-person work force. The Allen parents enjoy their family daily as all of their children with spouses and grandchildren live in Nauvoo

Carolyn Sue (Carrie) and her husband, Dave, are the parents of a fifteen year old daughter, Ashlie. Carrie owns and operates her own popular hair stylist business.

Charles Marcus (Marcus) and his wife, Kathy, are the parents of three children: Maya (7), Craig (6), and Lani (4). Marcus has worked on the Nauvoo Temple project with his father and is now taking special training as a piano technician and refinisher to improve his opportunities. He also teaches private piano lessons

Christina Bronwyn (Christie) and her husband, Michael, are the parents of three children, Andrew (6) , little Camille (born and died 1996), and Abby (4). She has returned to school to complete her degree in elementary education specializing in teaching socially challenged children.

Charlene Ruth (Charlene) and her husband, Curtis, are the proud parents of a healthy son, Luke, (December 2001). Charlene received her education in nursing but is now a stay-at-home mother enjoying her new son.